THE SUNDAY TIMES

Vitality

COOKBOOK

THE SUNDAY TIMES

Vitality

COOKBOOK

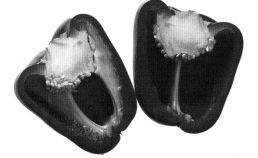

Susan Clark

HarperCollins*Illustrated*

Design copyright © The Ivy Press Limited 1999
Text copyright © Susan Clark 1999

Recipes devised by Erick Muzard

Published in Great Britain in 1999 by
HarperCollins*Publishers*
The HarperCollins website address is
www.**fire**and**water**.com

A CIP catalogue record for this book is available
from the British Library

ISBN 0 00 414086 9

Note from the Publisher
Information given in this book is not intended to be
taken as a replacement for medical advice. Any person
with a condition requiring medical attention should
consult a qualified medical practitioner or therapist.

This book was conceived, designed and produced by
THE IVY PRESS LIMITED
The Old Candlemakers
West Street
Lewes, East Sussex
BN7 2NZ

Creative Director: PETER BRIDGEWATER
Art Director: ALAN OSBAHR
Designer: BERNARD HIGTON
Editorial Director: DENNY HEMMING
Managing Editor: ANNE TOWNLEY
Project Editor: LORRAINE TURNER
Editor: NICOLA PRESTON
Illustrations: PIP ADAMS, JERRY FOWLER
Studio Photography: MARIE-LOU AVERY
Food Stylist: JACQUELINE CLARKE
Additional help with food styling: JOANNA FARROW,
FELICITY BARNUM-BOBB
Picture Research: LINDA MARSHALL

Reproduction and printing in Hong Kong by
HONG KONG GRAPHIC & PRINTING LTD

This book is typeset in Franklin Gothic and Bodoni

For those who helped me hear the call back – especially
Nicola – and for my travelling companion, Declan

The Publishers wish to thank the following for the use of
pictures:

A–Z Botanical Collection: p.20c.
Garden Picture Library: pp.18r, 158t.
Image Bank: pp.6l, 12c, 13c, 17l, 20l, 21t, 22cl, 22b, 22c,
24l, 26br, 27b, 28l, 160l, 168bl, 172r, 175t, 176b, 180l,
182l, 183b, 185t, 187br, 188b, 189t.
Science Photo Library: pp.14, 16c, 19cl, 24b, 158b, 161c,
168c, 181b, 184b.
Stock Market: pp.15t, 22l, 157bl, 174r, 177t.

contents

INTRODUCTION

We live in the Information Age and yet, in many ways, we have never been so ignorant about our health. Much of the traditional folklore that was used to prevent or fight disease long before the advent of modern drug-driven medicine has been lost or forgotten. Nobody has time to read food labels and, even if they do, some of the hidden ingredients, like the controversial genetically modified soya bean, have never been tested on humans anyway.

Biotechnology is the brave new science of the Millennium. Like the effect computers had on us at the end of the 20th century, it will radically change the way we all live and, especially, what we all eat. Yet even with these new products, we still don't really know what we are eating. Chemicals inevitably find their way into the food chain but current tests cannot even detect more than half of those known to be used in food production. There are no tests for what happens when these chemicals or other additives combine or when chemicals break down in the body and form new, usually dangerous, compounds called metabolites.

The biggest health risk we face every day is not getting behind the wheel of a car or boarding a transatlantic flight, but sitting down to a meal that has been so highly processed that all the nutritional value has been lost. What is left of the food is likely, in the long term, to make us ill.

Trying to be healthy has never been more difficult. Although we need to eat some fat to survive, including cholesterol which is important for the manufacture of vitamin D and for the sheath membranes that protect nerves, a low-fat diet is healthier than a high-fat one. Yet many of the so-called low-fat products on the shelves are still high in fat and have been pumped full of sugar and additives to make them tastier and more appealing to a palate that is used to refined foods.

So which is riskier? The fat or the additives? Nobody has much time to cook anymore and even if you do produce a healthy, home-cooked meal, the kids will probably sulk and demand junk food. In fact, we're all so busy the food makers can get away with almost anything because nobody has time to worry about what they are eating.

The battle to better health is going to be a long one but it will be well worth the effort. The number of degenerative diseases is on the increase, with some experts predicting that by the year 2030 everyone will experience some form of cancer before death. We are all living longer and people who have worked hard all their lives want to be well enough to enjoy the fruits of their labours as they age.

You can take anti-ageing supplements that may help to swing the odds in your favour, but the one thing we know that works for sure is diet. The idea of using food as medicine is as old as Hippocrates – the Greek father of modern medicine who said "Let food be thy medicine". Hippocrates did not, of course, mean mass-produced burgers and chips dripping in artery-blocking saturated fats. However, you can eat healthy versions of burgers – there's a recipe for them in the children's section of this book – but make them yourself so that you know exactly what you are eating.

Knowing what is on your plate is the key to this book and why you need to read it. Too often people take pot luck with the most important thing in their lives – their health. You don't have to be a health freak, but it makes sense to look after the body which, if you nourish it properly, will serve you better than any machine you might buy.

To help you choose a healthy diet, and even to modify your diet to give you protection against, or help you recover from, specific ailments, we have devised over 100 recipes and then analysed each one in detail for its nutritional benefits. Each recipe is also colour-coded to show which conditions it can help you to fight. A meal that is bursting with the B vitamins and vitamin C, for instance, is a good stress buster, while a dish that is packed with potassium will help lower

blood pressure, reduce allergies and give you greater mental clarity because potassium sends oxygen to the brain.

Scientific research is beginning to prove the benefits of old-fashioned treatments. Your grandmother, for example, may have believed that the culinary herb sage was a "cure-all" and could help soothe an elderly and confused person. What she could not have known is that it does this by restoring impaired vascular supply to the brain. It is now believed that sage can play an important role in treating Alzheimer's disease. Sage is also excellent for helping the digestion.

We have used herbs in almost every dish, but if you wish to try sage in particular, you can substitute it for the lavender in our Summer Honey & Lavender Crème Brulée (*see page 112*). It may sound strange but it is delicious, and shows that herbs can cross the artificial boundary between savoury and sweet dishes.

You will not find references to added salt in these recipes. When we say season to taste, we leave the option to salt or not to salt with you. Before you decide, however, remember that, while we need some salt in our diet in order to survive, we need less than 5g a day to stay healthy. To calculate the salt content of a dish in grams, multiply the sodium levels by 2.5.

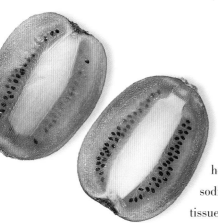

Sodium helps to maintain the acidity levels of the blood, keeps all the body's fluid levels healthy and is important for healthy muscles. However, too much sodium can cause fluid to be retained by the tissues, which can lead to high blood pressure and a risk of heart disease. This in turn can aggravate existing conditions such as kidney disease, heart problems and premenstrual disorder. The best advice is to be strict about limiting the amount of salt you use in your cooking and to avoid processed foods, which are almost always heavily salted.

Unless you buy organic produce, dairy foods can be contaminated by traces of hormones and antibiotics that are used in intensive farming to promote rapid growth and a bigger profit. To minimise the risk of eating chemicals that can upset the body's carefully balanced hormone levels and overburden the liver and digestive tract, we have suggested the use of substitute soya products in many of the recipes. When you buy these, make sure that they come from companies that do not use genetically modified soya beans; at least until someone does some testing on humans.

What this book does, like no other, is take all the guesswork out of what you are eating. No dish is in this book by accident. Every recipe has at least one and usually more nutritional benefits to commend it. Not only do we tell you, for example, that a dish is rich in vitamin A – an important antioxidant that is crucial for maintaining a healthy immune system and glowing skin – we also give you the precise percentage of the recommended daily allowance (RDA) for adults. In the children's meals, these figures reflect the percentage of a child's recommended daily allowance.

There is much dispute and debate about the RDAs because they are guidelines that show the

minimum amount of a nutrient you need to avoid becoming ill through a deficiency. However, they fall far short of the doses that will promote optimum health.

These doses, often referred to as the Optimum Daily Allowance (ODA), are much higher but not yet agreed by the experts. In many of our recipes, the amount of a vitamin or mineral supplied is much higher than the RDA. There is no risk of overload here – these dishes will help you to achieve optimum health and your body will flush out those nutrients it does not need.

Nowhere, in this book, will you find the word "calories" used in the context of losing weight. The best way to lose weight is to forget about dieting and adopt a healthy eating plan. When you switch to more wholesome, natural foods,

you will automatically drop to the optimum weight for your build and stay there. You will feel better and your clothes will look better on you. You can eat as much of these foods as you want so there's no feeling of missing out. You'll also have twice, probably three times, the energy you had before.

Most of us ignore our health until we have a scare and can no longer take it for granted. If you are one of these people, you are very important because once you start to change your approach to your health and your diet, you can lead by example. You really can influence and change what the people you love are eating. And that's where a healthier lifestyle has to start – in your own home, in your own kitchen, with the people you care about.

As a health columnist for *The Sunday Times*, I know people are interested in their health and are eager to learn more. I get 100 letters every week from people all over the world who are frightened of a number of degenerative diseases and are trying to take responsibility for their own health. Many of these people know that diet can help but are not sure where to start. It is for these people that we have written this book. When I say we, I mean myself and the French chef, Erick

Muzard, who devised the recipes in this book. I deliberately wanted to work with a chef who adores food because, above all else, eating should be one of the greatest pleasures in your life. I also wanted to work with someone who did not have any in-built leanings towards healthy but boring eating plans, because I wanted recipes that look and taste delicious and that people cannot wait to cook. What I wanted, and what I think a lot of us want, is an enjoyable way of getting and staying healthy, as if almost by accident.

At the end of our work on these recipes, I asked Erick what health lesson, if any, he had learned from our research and our arguments (especially about butter and salt). He did not hesitate. "Eat more fresh fruits and vegetables," he said. "Buy organic produce. And, if like me you love the taste of meat and cannot give it up, make sure you know at least where it comes from and take steps to reduce the amount of saturated fat you're eating." I no longer eat meat, but I couldn't have put it better myself.

Happy healthy eating.

Section**One**

A DIET FOR LIFE

The only true cure for any condition is the body's inherent ability to heal itself. To do this it needs your help. The risk of developing diabetes, heart disease, cancer and many other diseases that are linked to nutrition may be greatly reduced by improving your diet. By adapting the way you cook you can become your own healer.

Eating
Well

There is no such thing as the "perfect" diet, but for decades now experts have agreed that there is a simple way of eating, based on nutritious wholegrains and seasonal fruit and vegetables, that will dramatically reduce the risk of disease. It is the kind of diet that used to get a bad press, but with degenerative diseases claiming millions of lives in the developed world, and with so many of us functioning well below par, it is the kind of diet that is finally getting the attention it deserves.

Put simply, people who eat a high-fibre, low-fat diet rich in raw fruits and vegetables and wholegrains will live longer than those who fail to wean themselves from the high-fat, low-fibre, sugar-laden diet that has become the norm in industrialized countries and which is responsible for so much ill-health.

If you want a long and healthy life, you should also make sure your diet is rich in the essential fatty acids that the body cannot make itself and cut back on sugar, protein, salt, caffeine and alcohol.

FOOD FOR OPTIMUM HEALTH

Food is the source of energy for all physical and mental activity. Furthermore, the nutrients in the food we eat work together with our bodies to repair, maintain and even replace every cell in the body about once every four months. As you read this, you are making over 200 million new cells to replace the same number of worn-out, dying cells, and you will continue to repeat this process every minute throughout your life.

The human body is the most magnificent example of evolution, still capable of blinding science with its sophistication and efficiency. But it can only function at optimum levels if you look after it. Feed it junk and bombard it with toxins and it will struggle to keep you healthy, but eventually will give up.

The good news is you don't have to be a health fanatic to give your body the best conditions for optimum health. During your lifetime food fads will come and go, but if you keep to the following guidelines, which can be modified when you have special nutritional needs, such as in pregnancy or when your immune system is under attack, you will be doing everything you can to remain healthy.

Eat a diet that is as natural as possible with plenty of unrefined seasonal nuts, fruits and vegetables.

Wholegrains such as barley and rye are rich in protein and B vitamins.

BALANCED DIET

Wholegrains, such as corn, oats, barley and rye, and fresh fruit and vegetables should form the basis of your diet. Aim to eat eight servings from these foods a day (a serving is equivalent to one slice of bread or half a bowl of rice; half a standard side salad, a broccoli spear, or a small apple).

Most of the animal protein you eat should come from cold-water fish, especially salmon, tuna, herring and sardines, which contain essential fatty acids that help protect against cancers and heart disease. Eat oily fish at least three times a week. Eat meat sparingly – instead eat vegetarian sources of protein, such as nuts, seeds and beans, to help balance your diet.

When you eat dairy products, make sure they come from a good organic source and

Take your culinary inspiration from Nature.

when you cook with oil, use cold-pressed, virgin olive oil.

Minimize the amount of refined foods and sugar in your diet and try to avoid genetically modified foods and those that are pumped full of flavourings and additives, which have no nutritional value and may pose a threat to your health. Cut down, too, on stimulants like alcohol and caffeine, which tax the liver, affecting its ability to purify the blood and eliminate toxins.

Finally, you need plenty of uncontaminated, pure water to help your body flush out harmful toxins, so drink eight glasses of water a day. Drinking water before or after (but not during) a meal also helps to digest food properly.

ORGANIC, SEASONAL PRODUCE

We are the first generation whose bodies have had to cope with food grown in soil depleted of nutrients and an onslaught of toxins from the environment and from chemically processed food. Whenever possible, it is best to eat organically grown foods, because they contain more nutrients than highly processed foods and will be free of the pesticides, herbicides, chemical fertilizers, hormones and antibiotics that are used in intensive farming.

As well as eating food that has been produced organically, take your inspiration from the seasons. Throughout this book the emphasis is on fresh foods, because it makes sense to eat produce that has been grown locally and is in season. In the winter, for example, cook warming, nourishing dishes containing nutrient-rich nuts, root vegetables and tubers, such as potatoes. In the spring, which is a time of new growth and rapid expansion, eat energy-rich fruits and serve dishes piled high with delicious new shoots and vitamin-rich young greens.

REGULAR MEALS

Skipping meals sends the body into starvation mode encouraging it to stockpile fat reserves. It also results in mood swings. You should eat a moderate-sized breakfast, a large lunch and a moderate-sized evening meal. Keeping to regular eating habits will give you energy all day and will regulate digestion and sleep patterns. If you do need to snack, eat fruit, or nuts and seeds.

HEALTHY PREPARATION

Your body requires over 70 nutrients to function at its best and eating a variety of whole, fresh foods which have been tampered with as little as possible after harvesting will help provide many of these. Cooking can destroy some of these nutrients, so try to include some raw foods in your diet, for example a side salad every day. When you do cook, use gentle methods. Steaming, for instance, is less aggressive than boiling, preserving more of the vitamins and minerals in foods, and baking is better than frying.

10
point plan to improve your diet

1 Eat at least 3–5 servings of fruit and vegetables each day

2 Drink at least 8 glasses of water each day

3 Limit the amount of alcohol you drink (*see page 25*)

4 Drink no more than 5 cups of tea, coffee or cola daily

5 Eat a healthy breakfast

6 Eat fish at least three times per week

7 Eat no more than 2 portions of red meat each week

8 Cut down on ready-prepared foods you eat

9 Replace butter and animal fat with vegetable oil where possible

10 Do not add extra salt to food

Food
Groups

To maintain your health and fight off disease you need a balanced diet that includes all of the five main nutrient groups in the correct proportions and plenty of pure water. The five groups are carbohydrates, proteins, fats, vitamins and minerals. A diet based on nourishing wholegrains and fruit and vegetables with small amounts of fish, dairy products and meat will meet all your dietary needs and keep you in good health.

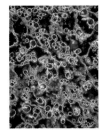

Starch molecules seen through a microscope.

CARBOHYDRATES

ALL SUGARS AND STARCHES INCLUDING THOSE FOUND IN BREAD, PASTA, RICE, CEREALS, PULSES, FRUITS, VEGETABLES, TABLE SUGAR, HONEY, SYRUP, SUGARY FOODS

Formed of carbon, hydrogen and oxygen, carbohydrates produce energy when the carbon molecules bind with oxygen in the bloodstream. It's best to eat complex carbohydrates such as bread and pasta, in preference to sugar – the other type of carbohydrate. Too high an intake of sugary foods such as puddings, cakes, chocolate, sweets and soft drinks, increases your risk of obesity, diabetes and heart disease. Complex carbohydrates are the best source of energy (glucose) that fuels all the body's functions. They have a more complicated molecular structure than simple sugars, which means they are broken down more slowly, releasing a steady flow of energy into the bloodstream. They help with the digestion and absorption of other foods, including protein and fat metabolism. Carbohydrates can prevent constipation, reduce the risk of cancer of the colon and regulate cholesterol levels.

Meat is composed of strands of fibre.

PROTEIN

MEAT, POULTRY, FISH, EGGS, MILK AND MILK PRODUCTS, WHOLEGRAINS, SOYA AND SOYA PRODUCTS, PULSES, BEANS, NUTS, CEREALS

Essential for growth and development, protein also provides energy. It is needed to make hormones, enzymes, antibodies and healthy tissues and to regulate the acid/alkali balance of the body. Protein is composed of about 20 amino acids, of which eight, known as "essential" amino acids, must come from food (the body can synthesize the rest). Essential amino acids are provided by "complete" proteins such as meat, fish, poultry, eggs, cheese and soya. "Incomplete" proteins, which include those from grains, pulses and leafy green vegetables, provide only some of the essential amino acids and therefore need to be eaten in combination (a Mexican wheat tortilla with refried beans for example) if the body is to obtain all the building blocks it needs to construct protein. Although meat and dairy products contain complete protein, you should eat them sparingly as they are high in fat.

The fat globules in milk are clearly visible in this view.

FATS

MONOUNSATURATED FATS, FOUND IN VEGETABLE AND NUT OILS SUCH AS OLIVE AND PEANUT OIL; POLYUNSATURATED FATS, INCLUDING SUNFLOWER AND SOYA OILS, OILY FISH, WALNUTS AND WHEATGERM; SATURATED FATS, FOUND IN MEAT AND DAIRY PRODUCTS

The food industry promotes low-fat food heavily because consumers are willing to pay more for such products (many of which are full of sugar and additives). Even so, the rate of obesity continues to climb. It has doubled in the last decade and the problem is now so bad that the World Health Organization (WHO) has declared it an epidemic. Fat, the most concentrated source of energy, is needed by the body; and not all fats are bad. For example, essential fatty acids promote good health. What is not needed, however, are large quantities of the wrong kind. Excess fat can also lead to high blood pressure, heart disease and cancer of the colon.

All fats are made up of fatty acids and are categorized according to the number of hydrogen atoms in the acids. Saturated fatty acids are the bad guys because they raise blood cholesterol levels. The US National Cholesterol Education Program recommends that saturated fats should make up no more than 10 per cent of your daily calorie intake. If you have heart or circulatory problems, even that is way too high.

Polyunsaturated fats are good for you, lowering overall cholesterol levels. However, they reduce the good type of cholesterol, which protects against heart disease, as well as the bad type that increases the risk. Monounsaturated fats, however, appear to lower bad cholesterol levels without reducing the amount of good cholesterol.

When polyunsaturated oils are altered through hydrogenation, the industrial process used in making margarine and other products, they form "trans-fats". Avoid products with these, as studies have found they help raise cholesterol levels.

Drink plenty of pure water.

WATER

Essential to life, water is involved in almost every function of the body. It transports nutrients to and from the cells and is crucial for all circulatory, digestive and excretory functions.

Water is also necessary for regulating the body's temperature. Few people drink enough water, and the biggest (and cheapest) favour you can do for your health is to drink eight glasses a day. Your skin will glow and you will see for yourself how it plays such a pivotal role in good health.

For optimum health, nutritionists recommend drinking steam-distilled water whenever you can. The distillation process eliminates bacteria, viruses, chemicals and other pollutants. If you suffer from digestive disorders, avoid carbonated bottled water because it can irritate the intestines.

FOR GUIDANCE ON THE REMAINING NUTRIENT GROUPS, VITAMINS AND MINERALS, SEE PAGES 16–17.

A Good Diet?

Your idea of a "healthy" diet may not be accurate. Compare the following:

Day 1
BREAKFAST
Grapefruit, orange juice, toast, reduced fat spread

LUNCH
Cottage cheese, large mixed salad, piece of fruit

DINNER
Skinned, broiled chicken, large salad, fruit salad

Day 2
BREAKFAST
Baked beans on wholemeal toast. Toast with scraping of butter and honey

LUNCH
Tuna fish and spring onion sandwich, red-and-green pepper salad

DINNER
Vegetable soup, grilled chicken, potatoes, green vegetables, slice of Brie and wholemeal bread

Day 1 is missing essential calcium, protein, zinc, selenium, potassium and fibre; but Day 2 is healthy and balanced to ensure that you get protein, carbohydrate, fat and fibre.

1 *Green vegetables*
2 *Pulses*
3 *Fruit*
4 *Meat*
5 *Dairy products*
6 *Potatoes*
7 *Fish*

Vitamins and Minerals

Vitamins and minerals are necessary for a whole range of body functions, yet they are frequently missing from the diet. You can eat all the right foods in the right proportions but there is still no guarantee that you will be getting all the nutrients you need. It is also impossible to harvest foods that are rich in vitamins and minerals from soil that has been stripped of all its goodness by intensive farming. You might therefore wish to consider taking supplements.

Manufacturing and refining techniques rob food of much of its nutritional value, while packaging processes, additives, pesticides and artificial preservatives – all designed to give food a longer shelf-life and a more appetizing look – replace nutrients with questionable chemicals. Switching to an organic, chemical-free diet wherever possible is the single most important step you can take towards reclaiming your health.

In an ideal world, you would get all the nutrients you need from your healthy, organic diet, but for most of us, the demands of a busy life make this almost impossible, however good our intentions. Entire families exist almost exclusively on convenience foods, and even the most dedicated disciples of healthy eating cannot always make sure every meal is properly balanced.

This means that supplementing your diet with vitamins and minerals is the next best method of staying well throughout your life. Supplements are no substitute for healthy, wholesome foods and you cannot use them to try to counter too many takeaway curries, but they are a useful adjunct to a nutrient-rich diet.

Chemical Bread

Consider this: a hundred years ago, a loaf of bread contained just five natural ingredients, which provided around 24 wholesome nutrients. Today, a commercial loaf is often an unsavoury cocktail of 100 constituents, including residues of chemicals from the packaging, preservatives, colourings and fungicides. Some may have three or four of the nutrients that have been stripped out then replaced, so the bread can be sold as "enriched" with fortifying vitamins.

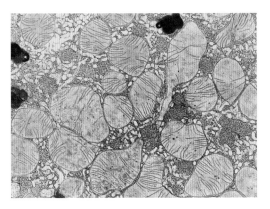

Close-up view of the mitochondria that oxidize fats and sugars to provide energy for body cells.

DO YOUR HOMEWORK

We spend £360 million a year on nutritional and herbal supplements in the UK alone, and in the US the complementary health market is estimated to be worth as much as $27 billion. There is a staggeringly confusing array of supplements on offer and I suspect many manufacturers are only too happy to blind us with jargon and pseudo-science. Supplements themselves go in and out of fashion, and many of us are further confused by terms like supernutrients and megavitamins. (The latter is used to describe very high doses of vitamins, which are prescribed to try to reverse an existing condition.) Supplements are not cheap and I am always shocked by the way people take them randomly. You wouldn't hazard a guess that the car needed an oil change, would you? So why take a stab in the dark with something as important as your health?

Even though we all need the same nutrients, the amount we require will differ according to our age, lifestyle, body weight, gender and levels of exercise. There is only one way to find out what you should be taking and that is to have a test.

Brown bread made with unrefined flour is more nutritious than white bread.

Supplements for Life

Vitamin A: Helps all cells reproduce normally and maintains healthy membranes and skin, which prevent micro-organisms that cause disease entering. Found naturally in green leafy vegetables, liver, dairy products and cod liver oil.

Vitamin E: Protects against heart disease and enhances the activity of vitamin A. A powerful antioxidant, it can slow down ageing and protect against blood clots. Found in wheatgerm oil, nuts, seeds, vegetable oils, egg yolks and leafy greens.

Vitamin C: Another potent antioxidant, which mops up the cancer-causing free radicals that also cause premature ageing. Promotes wound-healing and fights viruses. Broccoli and citrus fruits are good food sources.

Selenium: Activates an antioxidant enzyme called glutathione peroxidase, which may protect against cancer. Also regulates the thyroid hormones and protects against clogging of the arteries. Best sources are brazil nuts, organic bread and seafood.

Zinc: Essential for the synthesis of DNA, it is also a constituent of more than 300 enzymes involved in tissue repair, digestion, fertility, vision, cell reproduction and protein synthesis. Fights disease by bolstering the immune system. Foods rich in zinc include pumpkin seeds, tofu, eggs, oysters and other seafood.

Co-enzyme Q10: Found in the mitochondria (where energy is generated) in almost every cell and in highest concentrations in the heart and the liver. It can strengthen muscle and protects against heart disease and diabetes. Natural sources are spinach, broccoli, nuts, meat and fish.

Folic acid (Vitamin B8): Lowers levels of homocysteine: a by-product of metabolism now accepted as a more accurate indicator of the risk of heart disease than cholesterol levels. Also prevents birth defects. Found in beans, meat and leafy greens.

Manganese: Needed for healthy skin, bone and cartilage formation and crucial in protecting against osteoporosis. Too much calcium, iron and zinc will reduce its absorption. Good sources include nuts, seeds, pineapple, wheat bran and greens.

Magnesium: More people are deficient in this mineral than any other. Crucial for the formation of new cells, bone, protein and fatty acids, it also activates the stress-busting B vitamins, regulates energy production and controls insulin levels. Food sources include nuts and grains, fish, meat and leafy vegetables.

Probiotics: Dysbiosis ("leaky gut" caused by imbalance in the colon bacteria) can lead to pervasive yeast infections, lowered resistance to disease and irritable bowel syndrome. Probiotics help rebalance the gut flora. They are found in natural yoghurt.

Fish oils: These omega-3-rich oils contain compounds the body cannot make itself. They have anti-inflammatory properties and also regulate blood triglyceride levels to protect against heart disease. Good food sources include oily fish, especially mackerel, salmon, herring, sardines and anchovies.

A simple sweat patch test, arranged by a qualified health practitioner, will take the guesswork out of supplementing your diet and will save you a small fortune in the long run.

ANTIOXIDANTS

Many vitamins and minerals have potent anti-cancer and anti-ageing antioxidant properties. Antioxidant means the supplement can "mop up" the free radical molecules that are a normal by-product of metabolism and which, if left to scavenge in the body, can cause cell damage.

SYNERGY

While each vitamin and mineral has a specific function in the body, they are all interrelated and work together (nutritionists call this synergy). So changing your intake of one can, inadvertently, affect your absorption of another. Too much calcium, for example, can cause a deficiency in zinc, iron, magnesium and phosphorous by preventing their absorption in the body. This means that it is important to visit a nutritionist for a tailor-made list of supplements, rather than taking pot luck.

Supplements can enhance the action of an organic diet rich in oily fish, citrus fruits, garlic and green leafy vegetables.

Herbs and Spices

Herbs and spices don't just add flavour and interest to a dish – they can bring numerous health benefits, too. Ginger may help protect against heart disease, liquorice soothes digestive disorders and coriander helps detoxify an overburdened liver. Try to use fresh herbs whenever you can. The easiest way to have herbs to hand is to grow your own. Many herbs are easy to cultivate at home. You can then enjoy their revitalizing aroma in cooking and also every time you brush by.

Herbal Teas

Herbal medicine is completely natural and works by treating the cause of ill health, rather than the symptoms. You will benefit from herbs' healing power if you use them to flavour food, but if you want to use them properly as medicines to treat disease, you should take them as a tea. Simply add a large teaspoon of powdered herb to a cup and pour on boiling water. Infuse for 10 minutes and drink while hot. (Sweeten with honey if you like.)

If you cook regularly, the chances are you will already have a bountiful medicine chest in your kitchen store cupboard. Did you know, for example, that in India's traditional Ayurvedic medicine, basil is used to treat stomach, kidney and blood ailments or that cooking with cumin will help boost your body's ability to absorb other important nutrients? Spices too can enhance health and self-healing. Just one teaspoon (5g) of ground cinnamon, for instance, provides 61mg of bone-building calcium, 25mg of potassium, 1.43mg of vitamin C and traces of the antioxidant vitamin A.

WHAT IS A HERB?

A herb is any plant that is valued for its medicinal, culinary or aromatic qualities. As well as livening up a dull recipe, herbs can be used to relax, soothe and energize, as well as to target specific organs, fight infection, bolster natural defences against disease, and ease aches and pains.

Herbs can also be effective where conventional medicines are impotent. Antibiotics, for example, cannot eliminate viral infections, but many herbs can.

Herbal remedies are powerful and they make up three-quarters of all the medicines used in the world. Indeed, the very word "drug" comes from the early German word *droge*, meaning to dry, as in drying herbs. It is estimated that up to half of all prescription drugs either come

Cultivate your own herb garden to provide a supply of healing natural medicines all year round.

directly from plants or are chemical imitations of constituents naturally found in plants. Aspirin, for example, now considered a cure for conditions as diverse as heart disease and cataracts, is, in fact, a chemical imitation of salicin, an acid derived from the bark of the white willow tree. Even less exotic herbs such as parsley have an important role in promoting optimum health. This herb, which you can chew to freshen the breath after eating garlic, can aid digestion and clear congestion caused by coughs and colds.

NEW WAYS OF USING OLD FAVOURITES

The use of plants for healing goes back to prehistoric times. Our ancestors worked intuitively with herbs, which they harvested themselves. Today, new research illumines extraordinary properties of many everyday plants. Rosemary, for example, is a powerful antioxidant, which has been shown to strengthen heartbeat. Sage, which has

SAGE

impressive anti-ageing properties, can restore impaired vascular supply to the brain and may play a role in treating Alzheimer's disease. While such herbs are anything but new, Western herbalists are changing the way they use them. The old idea that only one herb should be used to treat a particular condition has been usurped by polypharmacy, or the practice of treatments based on combinations of different herbs.

THE WONDER HERBS

The idea of a "new herb" is a contradiction in terms because healing plants that have only recently become popular in the West have been in existence for thousands of years and used by traditional cultures throughout that time. Echinacea (pronounced Ek-in-a-shea) is a good example. Now one of the best-selling herbal remedies on both sides of the Atlantic, it was first used by the Native American Sioux Indians for snake bites and wound healing. A potent immune-booster, antibacterial and antiviral herb, it can also help psoriasis and eczema.

Staphylococcus aureus, a common bacterium, is kept in check by herbs such as garlic.

Also new to the West are the powerful immune-boosting medicinal mushrooms, shiitake, reishi and maiitake. The latter, which grows to the size of a basketball and is known as the dancing mushroom, is being marketed as an anti-yeast treatment for candida infections. Shiitake is used as a cancer-fighting agent in China and Japan (try Shiitake Soup, see page 36) and reishi is used to prevent heart disease.

Remember, although culinary amounts of herbs are safe, herbal remedies, like any medicines, can be very potent and should be handled with care. Particularly, if you are pregnant, breastfeeding or taking medication, see your doctor or a qualified medical herbalist first.

ROSEMARY

Top Ten Kitchen Herbs

BASIL

PARSLEY

GINGER

LIQUORICE

CORIANDER

NETTLE

Ginger: A spiritual and physical cleanser, good for coughs, colds, indigestion, travel sickness, morning sickness, arthritis and circulatory problems.

Basil: Stimulates the immune system to make more antibodies. Relieves many conditions, including asthma, arthritis, rheumatism and headaches.

Rosemary: A gentle liver tonic, it stimulates circulation, strengthens the heartbeat and is a good antidote to stress.

Sage: Astringent and antiseptic, it has powerful anti-ageing properties, enhances memory and may help protect against Alzheimer's disease.

Coriander: Antifungal and antibacterial action aids digestion and alleviates allergies and hayfever. Decongests the liver and eases cystitis and skin rashes.

Turmeric: May aid fat loss and boosts circulation. Energizes the immune system and speeds up wound healing.

Fenugreek: Relieves constipation, lowers cholesterol and reduces blood sugar levels. Soothes coughs, fevers, sore throats and menstrual pain.

Nettle: Protects against anaemia, allergies and hayfever, high blood pressure and heart disease. Can also alleviate the symptoms of prostate enlargement.

Garlic: Potent antibacterial agent, effective against colds, skin problems and digestive disorders. Can also help circulatory disorders.

Liquorice: Alleviates stomach disorders, bronchitis, sore throats, coughs, kidney problems and irritable bowel syndrome (IBS).

GARLIC

Food
Safety

You may think that you know what's on your plate but it's likely that you never have time to read the food labels on jars or ready-cooked meals, and even if you do, would you recognize what all those long chemical names really mean? They say that ignorance is bliss, but when it comes to the food you eat, it's downright dangerous. The more you know about how food is grown, prepared, processed, packaged and coloured, the more you will be able to protect your own and your family's health.

Flamingo feathers and beetles are just some of the unsavoury ingredients that can end up in our food.

Since 1940, when the per capita intake of chemical additives and preservatives was first recorded, the amount of artificial colourings added to the diet in the US has rocketed by 995 per cent. How do you know, for instance, that the loaf of "healthy" brown bread from the supermarket is not simply white bread dyed with caramel colouring? The answer is you don't.

AN ADDITIVE BY ANY OTHER NAME?

Most additives have to be declared, but there are several thousand flavouring additives that do not have an E number and do not have to be listed. Manufacturers know that consumers have become ultra-wary of anything that contains E numbers and so many fudge the issue by avoiding the use of numbers altogether. Instead, they give the ingredient its full chemical name and hope we are all too busy to read the label, let alone find out what that chemical is. Food processing aids, including the solvents and propellants that are used to carry additives into food, do not have to be declared, even though traces of these may find their way into the finished product.

How many vegetarians know that rennet, which is made from calves' stomachs, may be used in "vegetarian" cheese? Rennet contains an important enzyme called chymosin, which coagulates milk. Since 1992, many manufacturers of so-called vegetarian cheeses have used a genetically engineered enzyme produced in the laboratory. Genetic material from calf cells is inserted into a yeast which is then grown under controlled, laboratory conditions. The manufactured chymosin is said to be "nature identical" to the original and it is legally allowed in the UK to be used in the production of vegetarian cheese.

What do a Mexican cactus beetle, a flamingo feather and a burned vegetable have in common? They are all used to produce food colourings, which are then said to have come from "natural" sources. The beetle is crushed and the carcass used to make cochineal (E120), which has been linked with food intolerances, the flamingo feathers produce canthaxanthin (E161), now banned in food but still allowed in chicken feed to colour egg yolks, and those charred vegetables produce an additive called carbon black, which is as unappetizing as it sounds.

Look Before You Eat

Many of the additives in current use are simply presumed safe. Others have been deemed safe but are already suspected of causing problems. Others are still in the throes of being tested. If you, or any member of your family, suffer from asthma, hyperactivity, aspirin sensitivity, phenylketonuria or gout, you should avoid food additives, colourings and preservatives, and consult a nutritionist.

High-tech laboratory techniques allow scientists to grow animal cells for use in food manufacture.

FRANKENSTEIN FOOD

Most consumers do not like the idea of genetically engineered or irradiated foods. Such foods are very common in the food industry, for example soya and soya oil are constituents of over 7,000 everyday foods, so it is hard to avoid eating the controversial, genetically engineered version. (There is, to date, no evidence that modified soya is harmful to humans, although its effects on people have not been tested.) The idea of irradiation to prolong shelf-life has proved so unpopular that despite the fact the UK government made it legal in 1991, only one British company has a licence to do it, and then only on herbs and spices.

Sue Dibb, co-director of The Food Commission (an independent organization in the UK that lobbies for the consumer to be told the truth about food), is the author of *What The Label Doesn't Tell You* which warns that in Europe, several thousand tons of food are irradiated each year and nobody will say where it ends up. (Processed and restaurant foods are the obvious suspects.) If you read that book, supermarket shopping will never be the same.

The notion that bombarding food with gamma rays (irradiation) would make the food radioactive and toxic to consumers caused a big food scare. These fears proved to be unfounded. However, there are hidden dangers as highlighted, for example, by the case of a cargo of irradiated and lethal prawns shipped to Europe from the Far East. The prawns had been contaminated with cholera and, after tests, scientists found that while this process had indeed killed the bacteria, it had not destroyed the toxins they produce.

By law, any food or ingredient that has been irradiated must say so, except if it makes up less than 25 per cent of a compound ingredient. So food that may look fresh may be stale and stripped of most of its vitamins.

In the United States, fruit that has been waxed or sprayed with insecticide must say so. In the UK, you had better peel that shiny red apple, because it is probably covered in shellac, or E904 – an insect secretion – also used to glaze sweets and cake decorations. Or you could give it to your least favourite person!

Don't judge by appearances: healthy-looking apples, eggs and bread may all contain gruesome food additives.

Fast Food

With fast food restaurants on every corner, if you want to stay healthy it is important to wise up to their dangers. You can of course enjoy the occasional takeaway with family and friends, but on the whole this type of food tends to be laden with sugar, fat and flavour enhancers such as monosodium glutamate, so it makes sense to be careful about what you order. More rice and less korma may sound depressing, but if you persevere, you'll soon find that you have retrained your tastebuds.

Fast-paced modern living dictates that we eat more and more food from takeaway joints.

Barnstaple is a small, rural market town on the glorious North Devon coast of England. Once, there were no sinful takeaway restaurants to lead you astray, unless you count those good old British institutions selling cholesterol-laden fish and chips and worse – the kind of heart-attack-in-a-bag, grease-sodden street food that sends any nutritionist worth their salt into paroxysms of dire health warnings, but which remains so beloved of Britons everywhere.

I know this because I grew up here and, as a child, looked forward to the occasional treat of crispy battered cod and soggy chips. Today, children living in Barnstaple can persuade mum and dad to visit any one of 45 fast-food outlets, ranging from Italian to Indian. And, of course, there's McDonalds.

When I was growing up it didn't matter much if we sometimes ate what would now be called junk food, because the rest of our diet was so nutritious. Homegrown vegetables came from the garden, complete with mud and slugs. We were organic long before anyone talked about being organic, and we ate what was in season because that's all that was available – we didn't know anything different.

The picture is very different now. All over the world, fast food has become the mainstay of many families' diets. In one recent survey, a third of nutritionists questioned owned up to succumbing to a burger, pizza, Chinese, Mexican or Indian meal at least once a week. We eat, on average, an estimated 4kg (9lb) of crisp-type snacks per person every year and what is clear is that fast food is here to stay.

MAKING SENSIBLE CHOICES

Unlike supermarkets, takeaway restaurants have no legal obligation to tell you what's in the food that they stuff between tacos, pile high on to limp sesame buns or cram into crispy pitta bread. So, it's up to you to monitor what you eat and choose the healthiest options. Opposite I give you plenty of tips on how to do this.

As long as the rest of your diet is healthy and you exercise, there's no reason why you can't enjoy fast food from time to time. It's junk *diets*, not junk *foods* we need to worry about, and for those eating balanced and healthy meals most of the time, the odd burger, pizza, taco or cod and chips is not going to prove a fast track to the hospital morgue.

With takeaway outlets on every corner offering cheap, mouthwatering fat-laden food, is it any wonder that obesity is reaching epidemic proportions?

Top Ten Tips for a Healthier Takeout

1 The single most important health tip to reduce the number of empty calories and unhealthy saturated fats in your takeout food, is to order more of the more nutritious, carbohydrate dishes, such as rice, and to opt for steamed or lightly stir-fried vegetables instead of deep-fried fatty foods.

2 The first pizzeria opened its doors in New York in 1895 and pizzas are still the fastest-growing sector of the fast food industry. Make yours healthier by ordering regular crust (thin and deep pan are both higher in fat), going easy on the cheese and topping it with healthy vegetables.

3 Classic Chinese cooking is very healthy, but most takeaway joints corrupt these dishes to make them appealing to the Western palate. Watch out for and avoid dishes laden with animal fat, liberal sprinklings of sugar and monosodium glutamate (MSG).

4 Filling up on plain, boiled rice and noodles will greatly improve the nutritional value of your Chinese takeout. Avoid the egg-fried "special" versions, which can contain lots of unhealthy cholesterol-raising fat, sugar and empty calories. For your main dish, order steamed or stir-fried vegetables and chicken or prawns, which are lower in fat than beef, lamb or duck.

5 Avoid that old favourite – sweet and sour. Independent analysis by The UK Food Commission found a portion of sweet and sour chicken with egg-fried rice totalled 2,025 calories; almost 100g (¼lb) of fat plus generous dollops of sugar and salt.

6 Follow similar guidelines with Indian food: fill up on the bulky carbohydrate dishes. Instead of fatty naan breads, order dry-fried chapatis, which also contain valuable B vitamins and fibre.

7 Cream-based kormas and deep-fried bhajis may be delicious, but they are high in empty calories and unhealthy fat. Choose the dry-fried dishes instead.

8 If you must eat fish and chips, find a shop that cooks with sunflower or other oils that are low in saturated fats. Avoid those that use a saturated vegetable fat, such as palm oil, animal shortening fat or beef dripping. Ask for a small portion of chips and fill up later with a slice of wholemeal bread once you get home.

9 The burger gets a bad press, but you can make your meal healthier by leaving out the cheese, which is probably processed and full of additives and colourings. A quality burger is reasonably healthy: it provides protein, iron, zinc and vitamin B12. It is high in fat although it is a healthier choice than fried chicken. Steer clear of cheap burgers, which are loaded with added fats and unsavoury E numbers.

10 Make a trip to the burger bar healthier by saying no to the chips. Sadly, those thin French fries, often flavoured with saturated animal fats, are the worst kind of chips because proportionately there's less potato and more fat than thick-cut chips.

Mono-unsaturated sunflower oil reduces cholesterol.

A burger made from lean meat with plenty of salad is a healthy choice.

Stir-fried Chinese food is one of the healthiest takeouts.

Fat chips contain far less fat than their thin cousins.

Pitta and falafel with plenty of salad is a good choice (but skip the mayonnaise).

Safe Drinking

Drinking may be pleasurable, but the health benefits are minimal and the risks are enormous. Drinking alcohol in moderation can have physical and psychological benefits – but the key word is moderation. Alcohol is a stimulant. It causes health problems on its own account and also exacerbates numerous degenerative diseases. Safe drinking guidelines vary from individual to individual, but stick to one drink a day if you're female and less than three if you're male.

A drink or two a day with friends is one of life's little pleasures, but it's important to stay within recommended limits.

Guess the nationality of the researcher who won world-wide plaudits when he published research suggesting that drinking red wine will protect you from cancer, as well as from heart disease? He was French, of course.

I say "of course" because Serge Renaud, a researcher at the University of Bordeaux, is probably one of those Frenchmen enjoying what the rest of the world calls The French Paradox. It is a question that has taxed the best brains in the field of nutrition for years and which continues to divide experts.

How can the French, whose diet is notoriously high in saturated animal fats, rank only 17th in the world's league table of heart disease? Some researchers have suggested that the answer lies at the bottom of a red wine bottle. They believe that phenolic flavonoids, non-alcoholic substances found in grape skins, can prevent the build-up of LDL or "bad" cholesterol and plaque in the arteries, which can lead to a stroke or coronary heart disease. The reason red wine and not white wine is said to confer benefits is that red wines are made by fermenting grapes with their skins on. More recent research has questioned the verity of health claims made about red wine, with some scientists suggesting that many grape varieties lose their antioxidant potency with age. One study published by the Rowett Research Institute in Aberdeen suggested the antioxidant properties of a 12-year-old malt whisky last longer in the body than those of red wine.

RAISE A GLASS TO OLD AGE

A larger survey has confirmed what many studies have shown, that alcohol, in moderation, can help to lower the risk of fatal heart disease. This research, conducted by The American Cancer Society over a nine-year period, was originally initiated to monitor the effects of alcohol in relation to cancer, and documented the impact of a drink a day on almost half a million men and women aged between 30 and 104, whose average age at the start of the survey was 56.

It showed that it is in middle age when alcohol's contribution to a healthy heart is expected to pay off, outweighing concerns about its ill-effects, which include a slightly increased risk of cancer.

Drinking alcohol in moderation has been shown to have both physical and psychological benefits. It can help to reduce stress, decrease tension and anxiety and encourage more relaxed, pleasant feelings of sociability and unself-

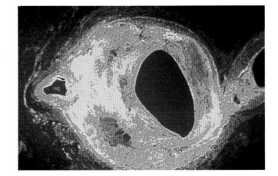

Plaque (coloured yellow) can build up in the arteries due to too much "bad" cholesterol in the blood. Substances in red wine may help prevent the build-up.

consciousness. In the elderly, alcohol has a range of benefits: it has been shown to stimulate a healthier appetite, promote regular bowel function and improve overall mood.

SENSIBLE DRINKING LIMITS

The subject of sensible drinking remains confusing, not least because people are still not clear what constitutes a "unit". To most of us, for example, drinking a bottle of wine (six UK units) sounds much worse than drinking three pints of beer (which is also six units, since half a pint of beer is one unit). To make matters worse, safe drinking guidelines vary wildly between countries and in any case, the same amount of alcohol can affect two people very differently.

The American Department of Health and Human Services, which probably has the strictest criteria, defines "moderate drinking" as no more than two drinks a day for men and one for women. A standard drink is deemed to be 350ml (12fl oz) beer, 150ml (5fl oz) of wine or 30ml (1½fl oz) of 80-proof distilled spirits. Each of these drinks contains roughly the same amount (12g (½oz)) of alcohol. In the UK, the guidelines are more generous but still fall way behind other European countries, especially France. UK men are advised to stick to 3–4 units a day, while women are restricted to 2–3. One unit is the equivalent of 8g (⅓oz) of alcohol.

Research has shown that, given the same amount of alcohol, women become more intoxicated than men. For this, blame biology. There is an enzyme that works in the stomach tissue to break down alcohol before it reaches the bloodstream. This enzyme is four times more active in men than it is in women. Also, women have, proportionately, more body fat and less body fluid than men. Because alcohol is more soluble in water than in fat, the same dose becomes more concentrated in the body of a woman than in the body of a man.

Based on research that shows that those with the lowest rates of mortality were men who drank less than three drinks a day, it makes sense to try to stay within these limits if you are a man. For women, research has shown that one alcoholic drink a day lowers the risk of coronary heart disease. For post-menopausal women, the protective effect of moderate drinking is considered to be due, in part, to an increase in oestrogen levels induced by the alcohol.

If you are planning to drive, the only safe drink is a non-alcoholic one. You should also try not to drink during pregnancy as even occasional drinking has been associated with birth defects.

6

rules for safe drinking

1 Men: drink no more than 3 units a day

2 Women: drink no more than 1 unit a day

3 Don't binge a whole week's allowance in one go

4 Have at least two alcohol-free days a week

5 Only drink good quality wine

6 At a party, alternate alcoholic drinks with water

ONE GLASS OF WINE IS ONE UNIT

A HALF-PINT OF LAGER IS ONE UNIT

ONE GLASS OF CHAMPAGNE IS ONE UNIT

ONE 'PUB' MEASURE (25ML/1FL OZ) OF SPIRITS IS ONE UNIT

Women's
Health

From anaemia and mood swings to PMT and menstrual irregularities, many health problems that affect women can be greatly helped by adjusting the diet. The biggest breakthrough in women's health is the discovery of phytochemicals – substances found in particularly female-friendly foods such as soya, broccoli and citrus fruits, which can help prevent and even reverse many conditions. These substances include phytoestrogens, which are helping women worldwide to regulate their hormones naturally.

Herbs for Women

Chaste berry (or agnus castus), wild yam, black cohosh, motherwort, raspberry, liquorice, lady's mantle and alfalfa are the eight most important herbs used to manage women's health problems including PMS, menstrual irregularities, infertility and menopause. Some can be used in food (*see also page 62*).

Vital compounds called phytoestrogens (or isoflavones), found naturally in foods, help to balance female hormones throughout the three main stages of women's lives.

Phytoestrogens all have an oestrogenic activity that is similar to the body's own oestrogen, but much less potent (only about 1/1,000th as strong). It is believed that phytoestrogens can protect the body from excess oestrogen, which otherwise leads to an increased risk of uterine and breast cancer. They are thought to work by supplanting the stronger oestrogen produced by the ovaries, causing it to be broken down by the liver and flushed out of the body.

From the late thirties to the end of menopause, oestrogen production slowly declines. The phytoestrogens have a role to play at this time, because they act as a natural oestrogen supplement, easing menopausal symptoms.

Population studies have shown that hormone-dependent diseases, including breast cancer, prostate cancer and osteoporosis, are all much lower in those populations whose diets are highest in phytoestrogens. Asian women, for example, who traditionally eat a diet that is high in soya, which is a powerful phytoestrogen, report so few menopausal symptoms that until relatively recently, linguistic experts could not find a word in their vocabulary that equated to the hot flushes which are all too familiar to women who eat high-fat, low-fibre diets. These magical substances, which can make all the difference between good health and debilitating health problems, are readily available in a wide range of everyday

foods – soya beans, chickpeas, lentils, citrus fruits, cruciferous vegetables such as broccoli, sprouts, cabbage and cauliflower, and liquorice, onions, garlic and chives. We have featured as many as possible in our recipes and if you do nothing else for your health, try to eat broccoli and cabbage at least once a week.

FEMALE-FRIENDLY FOODS

One of the most important phytoestrogens, and the one which has been studied the most, is called genistein. Found only in soya, it has remarkable anti-cancer properties. It not only inhibits tumour growth but, according to Japanese scientists, it also blocks the signal that triggers cells in the body to start multiplying so wildly out of control in the first place.

Genistein has been shown to destroy leukaemia cells in mice. It acts in a similar way to tamoxifen, the drug that is given to breast-cancer patients, but, as with all the natural

Soya beans, a staple ingredient in Asian cuisines, have helped to keep breast cancer at bay and other diseases that plague Western women.

phytochemicals, there are no side-effects. To benefit from this potent protection, eat at least one soya product every day.

Women need more iron than men. Beans, peas and leafy greens will all boost your iron intake. Liver is a good source, but it is high in cholesterol, making chicken a better bet. If you are worried you may be anaemic, get yourself tested because it is not easy to absorb all the iron you need from food. If you are iron-deficient, remember that vitamin C boosts iron uptake, so supplement your diet with 1g a day.

NO MORE DIETING

One national survey in the United States found that 40 per cent of women were trying to lose weight – almost twice the number of men. Constant and yo-yo dieting leave women at risk of becoming malnourished. Also, if you follow a strict calorie-controlled diet, the chances are depressingly high that the weight will all pile back on when you stop.

It is better to throw out the scales and start getting back the shape you want by regulating your eating habits. Eat three meals a day and, if you feel hungry in between, snack on fresh fruit, nuts, seeds and vegetables.

Push your trolley past the tempting but highly processed foods stacked on the supermarket shelves and make a beeline instead for the peripheral areas where the fruit and vegetables always look like the poor relations. Remind yourself, though, that they are not. These are the foods that will work with you and help you lose weight. If you introduce regular, moderate exercise three times a week into your schedule, with a rest day between your exertions, your weight will quickly stabilize. And if you stick to your new, healthier eating habits, the excess pounds will stay off.

I don't know how much I weigh and I don't really care. I monitor whether I am eating too little or too much by how my clothes fit. Dump the scales, adopt the holistic healthy eating guidelines at the start of this book and you and your family will never look back.

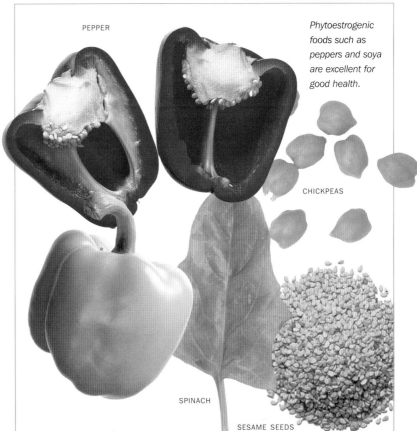

PEPPER

Phytoestrogenic foods such as peppers and soya are excellent for good health.

CHICKPEAS

SPINACH

SESAME SEEDS

The Three Lifestages

Any hormone-related disturbances you may suffer will vary depending on your age. Premenopausal women may complain of PMS, irregular menstruation, scanty or heavy periods, bloating, depression, irritability, breast tenderness, food cravings, pelvic cramps and an altered libido from up to 14 days before their period starts.

The hormonal balance changes in what is called perimenopause. The age this starts depends on many factors, including genetic makeup, lifestyle, diet, the number of children you have had and the amount of stress in your life. Generally, the first signs appear sometime between the mid-thirties and late forties. Periods may become either more or less frequent and you may have chronic fatigue, weight gain, water retention, mood swings, erratic blood sugar levels and insomnia. During menopause, oestrogen levels fall by up to 60 per cent and the secretion of progesterone stops. Tell-tale symptoms can include hot sweats, vaginal dryness, water retention, weight gain, insomnia, mood swings, dry and thin skin, brittle bones, fatigue, headaches, disturbed sleep patterns and a loss of sex drive.

All of the above symptoms, in the three stages of womanhood, can be alleviated by eating a healthy diet with phyto-estrogenic foods.

Men's
Health

Men often only consider their health when something goes wrong – they frequently look after their cars better than their own bodies. This is most unfortunate because men's health has never been more at risk: rates of prostate cancer are rising, sperm counts have fallen dramatically, and heart disease, which is often closely linked to poor lifestyle and dietary choices, is still the biggest killer of men worldwide.

Space travel has taught us valuable lessons about diet: over-refined food gave astronauts heart rhythm irregularities.

So many of the old wives' tales relating to food are true. Oysters, for example, really are aphrodisiac. Researchers have found that a man's sex drive can drop dramatically even if he is only marginally deficient in zinc, as this mineral is crucial to the production of the male sex hormone testosterone. And what are oysters a rich source of? Zinc. As well as being crucial for testosterone, zinc is also needed by the prostate gland, which makes seminal fluid for semen. It needs ten times more zinc than any other organ.

A healthy prostate weighs about 25g (1oz) and is the size of a small walnut. It can, though, enlarge painfully to the size of a plum. Although rare among men who eat foods rich in zinc and omega-3 fatty acids, prostate problems currently affect 10 per cent of all 40-year-olds and 80 per cent of all 80-year-olds. Prostate cancer is now the second most common cancer in British men, with only lung cancer causing more deaths. So, if longevity is your goal, start taking steps to protect against prostate conditions from your late thirties onwards. The good news is that there is a lot you can do. In one study of

200 men suffering from an inflamed prostate gland (a condition known as prostatitis), daily zinc supplements relieved the symptoms in 70 per cent of sufferers. In that 70 per cent, the prostate returned to normal or near-normal size within a few months.

Selenium has also been shown to help this condition. A study, published in the British journal *BJU International*, reported that men who took 200mcg of selenium each day were 63 per cent less likely to get prostate cancer than those who did not. What is worrying is that the selenium intake of most men falls way below this level. In the UK, for instance, the average intake is just 30–40mcg per day, less than a quarter of the recommended amount.

PEAK PERFORMANCE

Even impotence can be treated naturally. The best aphrodisiac, of course, is simply good health. But when 60 sufferers who had exhausted conventional treatments started taking 60mg a day of the potent Chinese herb *Ginkgo biloba*, half regained full potency within six months. The herb works by restoring circulation to all parts of the body. Both nettle and pumpkin are also said to help maintain healthy levels of male sex hormones.

MINERALS FOR HEART HEALTH

Heart disease is still the single biggest killer of men around the world, with some form of cardiovascular disease now affecting one in five American men and one in four British men. Minerals and vitamins play a crucial role in the healthy functioning of the heart for both sexes. The flow of calcium, sodium and potassium in and out of the body's cells creates electrical currents and these "charges" then travel along the nerves to "fire" the heartbeat. Vitamin E is involved in the transportation of calcium between

Herbs for Men

Saw palmetto, *the* herb for prostate health, helps to regulate hormonal changes that can lead to an enlarged prostate gland. It reduces conversion of the hormone testosterone to dihydrotestosterone, a compound that stimulates production of prostate cancer cells. Take 3 x 500mg capsules of powdered herb per day to avoid benign prostate hypertrophy (BPH), or to help relieve symptoms if you already have the condition.

cells. A deficiency in this important antioxidant has been shown to lower the heart's resistance to calcium, resulting in irregular beats. Vitamin E-rich foods include eggs, leafy greens, cold-pressed vegetable oils, almonds, hazelnuts, pecan nuts, sunflower seeds and sweet potatoes.

Magnesium is also important in the maintenance of a healthy heart because it helps to control the calcium and magnesium that pass through it. In fact, this mineral is so effective at keeping the heart pumping that heart-attack patients have magnesium injected into their bloodstream when they arrive in the emergency room to reduce the chances of deadly arrhythmias (irregular heartbeats).

Thanks to space travel and NASA's researchers, we now know the importance of potassium in heart health. Like magnesium, potassium affects the all-important heart rhythm. When two of the Apollo 15 astronauts, David Scott and James Irwin, both developed irregular heartbeats during a lunar

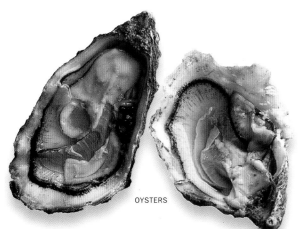

OYSTERS

mission, scientists worked out that the cause was a serious deficiency in potassium. Their food, which had been super-refined to keep it light, did not provide any of this vital mineral. Learning from this valuable lesson, when Apollo 16 was launched, the crew, who had been eating a potassium-loaded preflight diet, went into orbit with potassium-enriched foods and snacks.

In many refined foods, much of the potassium has been replaced by sodium, so you should compensate by eating plenty of potassium-rich fruit and vegetables.

MUSHROOM

EGG

BROCCOLI

PUMPKIN SEEDS

TOMATO

BANANA

ONION

Minerals for Men

Zinc: Best food sources of zinc, which is vital for cell membranes and testosterone production, include oysters, pumpkin and sunflower seeds, organic meat, mushrooms, eggs, wholegrain products and brewer's yeast.

Selenium: Needed to make proteins, it is also a constituent of sperm, so deficiency may be linked to infertility. Other signs of selenium deficiency include a depressed immune system, hair loss and chest pains. Food sources include wheatgerm, bran, tuna, onions, tomatoes, broccoli, kidney and wholemeal bread.

Magnesium: Essential for every biochemical process, including making protein and nucleic acids. Deficiency is common, especially in heavy drinkers and those who over-exercise. Symptoms include weakness, fatigue, vertigo, muscle cramps, nervousness and hyperactivity in children. To prevent magnesium deficiency eat brown rice, soya beans, nuts, brewer's yeast, wholemeal flour and pulses.

Potassium: Critical for energy production and a healthy heartbeat. Sweating induced by heavy exercise may cause a loss of potassium. Deficiency symptoms include vomiting, abdominal distension, muscular weakness, loss of appetite, low blood pressure and intense thirst. Eat fresh fruits, particularly bananas, and plenty of vegetables such as broccoli.

Section**Two**

THE RECIPES

"In India, those who prepare the family food are dedicated to their art and valued for their skill. Here, food and God (or Brahman) are one and the same. Preparing food thoughtlessly or ineptly is regarded as sacrilege. Those who prepare food have the Well-being of the whole household in their hands, for the sages say if we prepare food while harbouring angry or destructive thoughts, the food turns to poison."

Carrie Angus, *Food For The Wise*

KEY TO RECIPES AND BODY FUNCTIONS

Each recipe on the following pages has a series
of numbers to show which body systems the
ingredients in the dish will benefit or which
ailments they will help to counteract. For example,
the numbers 1, 2 and 6 by a recipe denote that
the dish will boost the immune system, digestion
and energy levels. The numbers 8 and 9 by a
recipe indicate that the ingredients will help to
prevent cancer or stress. The full list is as follows:

①	Immune system	⑥	Energy
②	Digestion	⑦	Depression
③	Skin and allergies	⑧	Cancer
④	Heart and blood	⑨	Stress
⑤	Teeth and bones	⑩	Hormones

Roasted Squash Soup with Fenugreek and Apple

When the high betacarotene content of this soup is converted to vitamin A in the liver, it can help to protect against heart disease and cancer. Fenugreek, which can help fight asthma, will also help lower cholesterol and aid digestion.

SERVES 6　　　　　　　　　　　　　　　　　　　　**②③❹❽**

25g (1oz) fenugreek powder

1.5kg (3lb 6oz) squash, quartered and deseeded

3 tbsp olive oil

1 large onion, diced

1 tbsp fresh root ginger, grated

3 garlic cloves, crushed

2 dessert apples, peeled and diced

1 litre (1¾ pints) chicken stock

freshly ground black pepper

juice of 1 lemon

1 Sprinkle half the fenugreek powder over the squash quarters and roast them in a very hot oven for 10 minutes.

2 Heat the olive oil in a large, heavy-based saucepan and cook the rest of the fenugreek with the onion, ginger and garlic until slightly golden.

3 Remove the squash from the oven and scoop the flesh out of the skins. Add the flesh to the saucepan along with the diced apple, chicken stock and black pepper.

4 Bring to the boil, then lower the heat and simmer for 40 minutes.

5 When cooked, blend, and then return to the heat to warm through. Just before serving, stir in the lemon juice.

6 Check the seasoning and dilute with fresh, organic apple juice if you prefer a less bulky texture. Serve hot with warm crusty bread.

FAT: 11G (17%) • PROTEIN: 6G (12%) • CARBOHYDRATE: 47G (16%) • FIBRE: 11G (45%)
VITAMIN A: 240% • VITAMIN C: 35% • CALCIUM: 10% • CHOLESTEROL: 0

Nettle and Sorrel Soup

Nettles were once so widely used in healing that whole fields were turned over to growing them outside medieval towns and villages. Rich in iron, they help build blood and can boost both circulation and energy levels. Sorrel is an excellent antioxidant. A gentle liver tonic, this soup will also aid digestion, but avoid this dish if you suffer from rheumatism, kidney stones or gout.

SERVES 6

2 4 6 9

400g (14oz) fresh nettles

250g (9oz) fresh sorrel

60g (2oz) butter (or soy substitute)

3 large shallots, diced

40g (1½oz) organic white flour

1.5 litres (2½ pints) stock (chicken or vegetable)

pinch of freshly grated nutmeg

freshly ground black pepper

juice of 1 large lemon

200ml (7fl oz) cream (or soy substitute)

1 Bring a large, heavy-based saucepan of water to the boil and blanch the nettles and the sorrel for 3–4 minutes. Drain, squeeze out all the liquid and blend to a smooth paste in a food processor.

2 In another large, heavy-based pan, heat the butter, add the shallots and cook until soft. Add the flour and cook for 3 minutes, taking care not to let the mixture discolour.

3 Stir in the nettle and sorrel paste, the stock, nutmeg and seasoning, and cook for 8 minutes. Just before serving, add the lemon juice.

4 Pour into warmed bowls and decorate with a swirl of cream (or cream substitute). Serve with warm Pumpkin Bread (*see page 122*).

FAT: 16G (24%) • PROTEIN: 5G (10%) • CARBOHYDRATE: 14G (5%)
FIBRE: 3G (14%) • FOLATE: 100% • VITAMIN C: 70% • IRON: 20%
CHOLESTEROL: 15%

Aigo-Boulido (Creamy Garlic) Soup

The ancient Egyptians fed garlic to the workers who built the pyramids, knowing only that it was a kind of miracle cure-all. In fact, it is a powerful antibiotic and good for the heart – two or three cloves a day can reduce your risk of a heart attack. By boosting immunity, garlic can protect against colds. It is also said to have potent anti-cancer properties.

SERVES 6

1 2 3 4 7 9

12 garlic cloves, crushed

2 tbsp olive oil

1 litre (1¾ pints) chicken (or vegetable) stock

1 bay leaf

60g (2oz) fresh sage leaves, finely chopped

3 egg yolks

freshly ground black pepper

10 slices French baguette

1 Blend the garlic and the olive oil to form a smooth paste.

2 Bring the stock to the boil in a large, heavy-based pan and add the garlic paste, bay leaf and sage. Bring to the boil, reduce the heat and simmer for 15 minutes.

3 In a small bowl, whisk the egg yolks together with a little of the soup, then add the mixture to the pan, stirring. Season to taste.

4 Grill the slices of French baguette and serve the soup with these slices floating on the top. (To make a more substantial dish, you can add boiled potatoes.)

FAT: 9G (14%) • PROTEIN: 5G (10%) • CARBOHYDRATE: 14G (5%) • FIBRE: 5G (19%)
VITAMIN A: 15% • CALCIUM: 15% • IRON: 20% • CHOLESTEROL: 36%

Monkfish, Leek and Saffron Soup

Fish is an excellent source of heart-protecting potassium and cancer-fighting selenium. It also contains the essential fatty acids, omega-6 and omega-3, that your body cannot make but must get from your diet. The healthiest ratio of these fats is 5:1 in favour of omega-6: this dish provides the perfect proportions in that ratio.

SERVES 6   ❶ ❸ ❹ ❽ ❾

1 medium-sized orange	700g (1lb 8oz) monkfish tails, cut into 2cm (½ in) pieces
10 strands of saffron	
2 tbsp olive oil	1 litre (1¾ pints) fish stock
1 large onion, finely diced	freshly ground black pepper
300g (10½oz) leeks, sliced	
3 garlic cloves, crushed	6 sprigs of fresh chervil, to garnish
300ml (½ pint) white wine	

1 Peel the orange very thinly with a vegetable peeler. Add the saffron to a little boiling water and leave to infuse.
2 Heat the olive oil in a heavy-based saucepan and, when hot, add the onion, leeks and garlic. Cook, stirring, until soft but not discoloured.
3 Add three-quarters of the fish, and the white wine, orange peel, fish stock and saffron strands, together with their water. Leave to simmer gently for 30 minutes.
4 When cooked, skim the orange peel off the surface, then blend the soup until smooth and creamy.
5 Return to the saucepan and add the reserved monkfish. Simmer gently for six minutes. Season and sprinkle with chervil leaves. Eat with crusty wholemeal bread.

FAT: 49G (75%) • PROTEIN: 22G (44%) • CARBOHYDRATE: 10G (3%)
FIBRE: 1G (5%) • VITAMIN C: 15% • OMEGA-6 FATTY ACIDS: 5.5G
POTASSIUM: 149% • SELENIUM: 67% • CHOLESTEROL: 10%

Shiitake Soup

Brown, beefy shiitake mushrooms have been eaten for more than 2,000 years in Japan. They stimulate the immune system to produce more interferon – a substance that helps the body to fend off both viral attacks and cancer. Shiitake mushrooms, which do not lose their nutritional value when cooked, help lower blood cholesterol and are also a good source of vitamin D, which, in turn, boosts the absorption of bone-building calcium.

SERVES 6   ❶ ❹ ❺ ❾

250g (9oz) smoked tofu, diced	*For the stock:*
125g (4 oz) shiitake mushrooms, sliced	2 dried chillies, chopped
	35g (1¼oz) tamarind pulp
4 tbsp chopped fresh coriander	kaffir lime leaves
1 bunch chopped fresh watercress	1 onion, chopped
	1 lemon grass stalk
1 medium-sized red chilli, sliced, to garnish	2.5cm (1 in) fresh root ginger, grated
	1 litre (1¾ pints) water

1 Boil all the stock ingredients together for 10 minutes. Drain through a fine sieve. Reserve the liquid and discard the contents of the sieve.
2 Stir-fry the tofu in a wok for a few minutes, then add the stock, shiitake mushrooms and coriander. Boil for 5 minutes.
3 Add the watercress and cook for another 2 minutes. Serve very hot with slices of fresh red chilli on top.

For variety, you can also make this soup with oyster mushrooms instead of shiitake.

FAT: 1.5G (3%) • PROTEIN: 4G (8%) • CARBOHYDRATE: 11G (4%) • FIBRE: 1G (6%)
VITAMIN C: 25% • VITAMIN D: 27.6% • CHOLESTEROL: 0

Cannellini Bean Soup

Beans are a rich source of soluble fibre, which helps to remove fat from the wall of the colon, flush out toxins from the body, lower cholesterol and stabilize blood-sugar levels. It can help to prevent cancer of the colon, constipation, haemorrhoids and obesity. Cabbage contains high levels of vitamin C, which is a powerful antioxidant that can help fight cancer too.

SERVES 6   ❷ ❸ ❹ ❺ ❽

400g (14oz) dried cannellini beans

2 tbsp chopped fresh sage

1 red onion

2 garlic cloves, finely chopped

2 tbsp olive oil

100g (3½oz) pancetta, diced

35g (1¼oz) cumin seeds

1 medium-sized white cabbage, sliced into strips

1 litre (1¾ pints) chicken (or vegetable) stock

1 bay leaf

50g (1¾oz) fresh flat-leaved parsley, chopped

freshly ground black pepper

1 Soak the beans for 24 hours and then place in a large saucepan full of water with the sage and half the red onion, roughly cut. Bring to the boil and simmer for 1–1½ hours until tender. Dice the rest of the onion.

2 In a large, heavy-based saucepan, fry the diced onion and the garlic in the olive oil until tender. They should be a golden colour.

3 Add the pancetta, cumin seeds and white cabbage to the saucepan and cook, stirring, for 3–4 minutes.

4 Add the cooked beans, stock, bay leaf and parsley. Season and cook for another 20 minutes. Serve with garlic and rosemary French bread. (To make: crush 4 cloves of garlic and 4 sprigs fresh rosemary in 3 tbsp olive oil. Slice a French baguette lengthways. Spread the garlic paste on the cut side and grill. Cut into portions.)

FAT: 57G (46%) • PROTEIN: 12G (24%) • CARBOHYDRATE: 28G (9%) • FIBRE: 11G (42%)
VITAMIN C: 140% CALCIUM: 30% • IRON: 45% • CHOLESTEROL: 5%

STARTERS

Grilled Figs with Parma Ham and Watercress

High-fibre figs have been shown to help shrink cancer tumours. Their juice also helps digestion, acting as a natural laxative. Both figs and watercress are good sources of beta-carotene, which is converted in the body to vitamin A. This vitamin, which is a powerful antioxidant, can protect against cancers, skin disorders (including acne) and eye problems.

SERVES 6   ① ② ③ ⑧ ⑨

6 fresh figs

2 tsp olive oil

2 bunches fresh watercress, chopped

10 fresh mint leaves, chopped

6 slices Parma ham, cut into strips

60g (2oz) fresh Parmesan cheese

For the dressing:

2 tsp balsamic vinegar

4 tsp olive oil

1 tsp pesto sauce

freshly ground black pepper

1 Cut the figs in half lengthways, brush them with olive oil and cook, skin-side up, on a griddle pan for 2 minutes. Keep warm.

2 To make the dressing, mix the balsamic vinegar with the olive oil and pesto sauce. Season to taste.

3 Arrange the watercress and mint leaves on a large, flat serving dish. Place the grilled figs on the bed of leaves and arrange slices of Parma ham on the top. Drizzle the dressing over the whole dish.

4 Using a potato peeler, shave slices of Parmesan cheese over the ham and figs and serve.

Vegetarians can serve this dish without the meat. For variety, meat-eaters can substitute chorizo (Spanish sausage) or smoked chicken.

FAT: 14G (14%) • PROTEIN: 10G (20%) • CARBOHYDRATE: 12G (4%) • FIBRE: 3G (10%)
VITAMIN A: 25% • VITAMIN C: 15% • CALCIUM: 20% • CHOLESTEROL: 10%

Marinated Raw Vegetables with Olive Oil and Herbs

Everyone knows that raw vegetables provide plenty of fibre, but did you know you can get iron and copper from mushrooms? Or that fennel provides plenty of potassium, which is needed to regulate blood pressure? This dish also provides vitamin B6, which is crucial for healthy blood and for making antibodies to fight disease. Loaded with vitamin A, it is a simple but potent anti-cancer recipe.

SERVES 6 ① ② ③ ④ ⑤ ⑧

300g (10½oz) fennel bulb, cut into 5cm (2in) strips

1 red pepper, cut into 5cm (2in) strips

1 green pepper, cut into 5cm (2in) strips

200g (7oz) celery, cut into 5cm (2in) strips

100g (3½oz) carrots, cut into 5cm (2in) strips

250g (9oz) button mushrooms

2 shallots, sliced into rings

40g (1½oz) small capers

75g (2¾oz) black olives, pitted

freshly ground black pepper

For the marinade:

5 garlic cloves, chopped

125ml (4fl oz) olive oil

2 drops Tabasco sauce

90ml (3fl oz) white wine vinegar

25g (1oz) chopped fresh chives

25g (1oz) chopped fresh chervil

25g (1oz) chopped fresh coriander

1 Mix all the vegetables, the shallots, capers and olives together in a large, flat glass dish.

2 To make the marinade, combine all the ingredients, reserving a quarter of the chopped herbs for a garnish. Pour over the vegetable mix, making sure all the vegetable strips are completely covered. Refrigerate for at least 12 hours.

3 Just before serving, sprinkle the reserved fresh herbs over the vegetables and season. Serve with warmed ciabatta bread.

This dish can form the base for a range of starters and supper dishes. You can also mix it with wholemeal pasta or couscous for a picnic lunch.

FAT: 22G (34%) • PROTEIN: 3G (6%) • CARBOHYDRATE: 13G (4%)
FIBRE: 4G (17%) • VITAMIN A: 120% • VITAMIN B6: 13%
VITAMIN C: 80% • IRON: 10?% • POTASSIUM: 64% • CHOLESTEROL: 0

Grilled Mackerel with Green Sauce

Protein-rich and high in immune-boosting and cancer-protecting vitamin C, this dish also provides omega-3, an essential fatty acid that has been shown to shrink cancer tumours and protect against lung, breast and prostate cancers. Fatty acids, which are typically missing from most Western diets, can also boost memory and reduce the severity of migraine headaches in some sufferers.

SERVES 6 ① ③ ④ ⑧ ⑩

6 small mackerel, scaled and gutted

1 large onion, roughly chopped

5 garlic cloves

5 fresh green chillies

75g (2¾oz) fresh coconut flesh

4 tbsp fresh coriander, chopped

1 tsp ground cumin

juice of 2 fresh limes

2.5cm (1in) fresh root ginger, chopped

1 tsp sugar (optional)

1 tsp salt

1 Slash the mackerel three times diagonally on each side. Put all the other ingredients in a food processor and blend to make a smooth paste.

2 Baste the fish with the paste and grill for 5–7 minutes on each side, under a medium heat, until the green sauce coating starts to bubble and the fish flesh flakes easily. The sugar will make the sauce shiny but is optional.

You can also use red snapper, sardines, or salmon fillets.

FAT: 13G (19%) • PROTEIN: 82G (164%) • CARBOHYDRATE: 10G (3%)
FIBRE: 3G (10%) • VITAMIN A: 70% • VITAMIN C: 170% • IRON: 45%
CHOLESTEROL: 70%

Shiitake Paté

Used in clinical trials to boost the immune response of HIV patients, shiitake mushrooms contain a polysaccharide called lentinan, which has been shown to slow the growth of cancer tumours in animals. They also lower cholesterol and help to prevent heart disease. Magnesium, known as the anti-stress mineral, is provided mainly by the shiitake mushrooms.

SERVES 4–6   ① ② ③ ④ ⑤ ⑥ ⑨ ⑩

100g (3½oz) fresh or dried shiitake mushrooms

2 tsp sesame seeds

1 large potato, cut into chunks

1 tsp sesame oil

3 large shallots, diced

2 tsp low-fat yogurt

juice of 1 lemon

2 tsp soy sauce

freshly ground black pepper

1 If you are using dried mushrooms, soak them in hot water for 20 minutes. If using fresh mushrooms, clean them with a small vegetable brush. Slice or dice the mushrooms.

2 In a dry pan, quickly brown the sesame seeds. Boil the potato chunks for 15–20 minutes, or until tender. Heat the sesame oil in a wok and cook the mushrooms and shallots until slightly brown.

3 When all the ingredients are cooked, put them in a food processor with the low-fat yogurt, lemon juice, soy sauce and browned sesame seeds. Blend until puréed. Season and chill for 2 hours before serving. Serve with warm mixed grain toast.

FAT: 2.5G (4%) • PROTEIN: 5G (10%) • CARBOHYDRATE: 31G (10%)
FIBRE: 4G (17%) • VITAMIN C: 20% • MAGNESIUM: 20% • CHOLESTEROL: 0

Grilled Goats' Cheese on Lambs' Lettuce

A healthy immune and nervous system both depend on manganese, which also helps regulate the sex hormones, brain function and blood-sugar levels. Bread is an excellent source. The goats' cheese provides selenium, a powerful antioxidant, which plays a crucial role in prostate health.

SERVES 6   ① ② ④ ⑤ ⑦ ⑧ ⑨

2 medium-sized cooking apples, cored and diced

1 pinch of cinnamon

12 slices of granary/mixed grain bread

200g (7oz) goats' cheese, cut into 12 rounds

400g (14oz) lambs' lettuce salad leaves

100g (3½oz) raw beetroot, grated

For the dressing:

4 tbsp vinegar

1 garlic clove, crushed

freshly ground black pepper

1 tsp wholegrain mustard

1 tsp honey

120ml (3¾fl oz) olive oil

1 Put the apple in a saucepan with 2 tbsp water and the cinnamon. Cook over a gentle heat for 10 minutes until the apples are puréed, then leave to cool.

2 Cut 12 discs from the granary bread with a round cutter. Spread the apple purée over the bread discs, place the cheese on top and arrange on a flat baking tray.

3 To make the salad dressing, mix together the vinegar, garlic, pepper, mustard and honey. Add the olive oil, whisking constantly.

4 Put the goats' cheese toast under the grill and cook until the cheese is melted and golden brown.

5 Toss the salad leaves and the grated beetroot thoroughly with the dressing. Arrange on a flat dish and place the goats' cheese toast on top.

FAT: 30G (46%) • PROTEIN: 12G (24%) • CARBOHYDRATE: 35G (12%)
FIBRE: 8G (31%) • MAGNESIUM: 14% • MANGANESE: 7.6% • SELENIUM: 1.6%
CHOLESTEROL: 10%

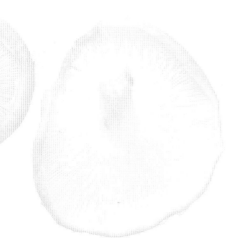

Marinated Sardines with Pine Nuts

Sardines are the richest natural source of omega-3 fatty acids, which can help prevent arthritis and breast cancer. Pine nuts are a good source, too. The fish also provides vitamin B12, which can improve memory and is essential for fertility and for building healthy blood and tissue.

SERVES 6   ② ③ ④ ⑦ ⑩

12 fresh sardine fillets, boned and scaled	*For the sauce:*
freshly ground black pepper	**6 garlic cloves**
	60g (2oz) pine nuts
125ml (4oz) olive oil	**1 tsp chopped fresh basil**
juice of 3 large lemons	**60ml (2fl oz) olive oil**
3 tbsp chopped fresh basil	**juice of 1 lemon**
	1 pinch cayenne pepper

1 Lay the sardine fillets skin-side up in a dish and season. Mix together the olive oil, lemon juice and chopped basil (reserving a little for garnish). Pour over the top of the fish and chill for at least 3 hours. The acid in the lemon juice 'cooks' the fish.

2 Meanwhile, make the sauce. Add all the ingredients to a food processor, season and blend until smooth. Check the seasoning and chill.

3 When the fillets are ready the flesh will have changed from brown to white. Serve them on slices of thick toasted brown bread, garnished with chopped basil and with the sauce on the side in a ramekin dish.

FAT: 24G (38%) • PROTEIN: 13G (26%) • CARBOHYDRATE: 4G (1%)
FIBRE: 1G (8%) • VITAMIN B3: 37% • VITAMIN B12: 261%
VITAMIN C 15% • CHOLESTEROL: 11%

Tartare of Salmon with Lime Juice

The Japanese, who regularly eat raw fish, have some of the lowest rates of heart disease in the world. The potassium in the salmon will help lower blood pressure, flush out toxins, regulate heartbeat and alleviate allergies. Stress, coffee, alcohol and sugar all deplete the body's potassium levels, so it is important to eat potassium-rich foods regularly.

SERVES 6   ① ③ ④ ⑨

400g (14oz) salmon fillet	**juice of 3 limes**
400g (14oz) tomatoes	**1 tsp chopped fresh basil**
freshly ground black pepper	**1 tsp chopped fresh parsley**
1 tsp green peppercorns	**120ml (4fl oz) olive oil**
2 large shallots, diced	**50g (1¾oz) low-fat yogurt**

1 Skin and bone the salmon fillet or ask your fishmonger to do it for you. Dice the salmon finely and reserve in the refrigerator. Steep the tomatoes in boiling water for 1 minute. Remove, skin and dice them.

2 In a large bowl, combine the diced salmon, pepper, green peppercorns and shallots. Add the lime juice, half the chopped basil, the parsley, the low-fat yogurt and 60ml (2fl oz) of the olive oil. Leave to stand in the refrigerator for an hour.

3 Mix the diced tomatoes with the rest of the basil and olive oil to create the sauce. Place the salmon mixture in the middle of a plate with the tomatoes around it. Sprinkle with freshly ground black pepper.

For a Thai-style taste, substitute coconut milk for the low-fat yogurt.

FAT: 34G (52%) • PROTEIN: 22G (44%) • CARBOHYDRATE: 15G (5%)
FIBRE: 3G (12%) • VITAMIN C: 50% • IRON: 15% • POTASSIUM: 50%
CHOLESTEROL: 12%

Oriental-style
Oysters with Spinach

Oysters are the richest food source of zinc, which protects not only the prostate, but all the reproductive organs. It also helps to prevent acne, boosts the immune system and accelerates wound-healing. Zinc works best in tandem with the anti-cancer, antioxidant vitamin A, which is supplied in abundance by this recipe. The presence of zinc increases the absorption of vitamin A. The spinach acts as a general blood tonic and will aid digestion.

SERVES 6　　　　① ② ③ ❹ ⑤ ⑥ ⑦ ❽ ❾ ⑩

12 large oysters

12 large spinach leaves

100g (3½oz) carrots, cut into long strips

100g (3½oz) leeks, cut into long strips

2 tbsp soya cream

1 pinch of curry powder

freshly ground black pepper

20g (¾oz) fresh chervil

200g sea salt to rest the oysters on for cooking: do not eat

1 Clean the oysters. Open them and pass the juice through a fine sieve. Remove the hard stalks of the spinach, wash the leaves and blanch (cook briefly) for a few minutes in boiling water. When softened, place the wilted leaves on a clean tea towel to drain.

2 Detach the oysters from their shells and wrap them in the middle of a spinach leaf. Return them to their original shells, pouring a little of their juice back over them.

3 Cook the carrots and leeks for about 5 minutes in boiling water, or until tender. Put the sea salt in an oven-proof dish and arrange the oysters on top. Place them in a warm oven (140°C/275°F/Gas mark 1) and cook for 5 minutes.

4 When cooked, pour the juice off each oyster into a saucepan. Add the soya cream, curry powder and black pepper. Bring to the boil and simmer for 1 minute to reduce the sauce.

5 To serve, place two oysters on each plate and pour a little of the sauce over each oyster. Pile the cooked vegetables and the chervil high on top. Serve with nutty rye bread.

FAT: 5G (7%) • PROTEIN: 13G (26%) • CARBOHYDRATE: 12G (4%) • FIBRE: 1G (6%)
VITAMIN A: 120% • IRON: 70% • ZINC: 100% • CHOLESTEROL: 30%

SALADS

Chickpea, Lime and Coriander Salad

Lime, coriander and, to some extent, chickpeas are good sources of vitamin C, which is crucial for the growth and repair of body tissues and which also helps the body to absorb iron. It accelerates healing after surgery, wards off the common cold and helps lower blood cholesterol. This recipe is particularly helpful if you smoke, because each cigarette destroys 25mg of vitamin C. The chickpeas are also an excellent source of both fibre and potassium.

SERVES 6   ① ② ③ ④ ⑤ ⑥ ⑧ ⑨

800g (1lb 12oz) dried chickpeas

1 large red onion, thinly sliced

1 red pepper, diced

1 green pepper, diced

2 tbsp fresh coriander, chopped

For the dressing:

3 garlic cloves, crushed

100ml (3½fl oz) olive oil

juice of 4 limes

1 Soak the chickpeas for 12 hours and cook them in unsalted water until tender (this may take up to 4 hours, though 2 is more usual). Skim the scum from the top from time to time. Alternatively, use ready-cooked chickpeas.
2 Combine the cooked chickpeas with the sliced onion, the diced peppers and the chopped coriander.
3 To make the dressing, mix together all the ingredients, then pour it over the chickpeas. Toss gently. Leave the salad to rest for at least 2 hours before eating. Serve with Irish wheaten bread.

FAT: 24G (34%) • PROTEIN: 27G (52%) • CARBOHYDRATE: 87G (29%) • FIBRE: 100%
VITAMIN C: 150% • IRON: 50% • POTASSIUM: 160% • CHOLESTEROL: 0

Roasted Nori (Seaweed) Salad

Magnesium helps the body to burn fat and produce energy. It is frequently lacking in post-menopausal women and has also been identified as a contributory factor in premenstrual syndrome. This Japanese seaweed salad can help to restore normal levels. A fifth of elderly people who take diuretics have a sodium deficiency, which the soy sauce can help to correct.

SERVES 6 ① ④ ⑤ ⑥ ⑦ ⑧ ⑨ ⑩

600g (1lb 5oz) cooked white rice

125g (4oz) Nori, roasted (see below) and flaked

2 tsp sesame oil

1 small courgette, grated

½ red pepper, diced

½ green pepper, diced

40g (1¼oz) sesame seeds, toasted

2 large onions, finely diced

2.5cm (1in) fresh root ginger, grated

For the dressing:

6 garlic cloves, crushed

2 tbsp rice vinegar

3 tbsp soy sauce

1 tsp honey

1 To make the dressing, whisk the crushed garlic, vinegar, soy sauce and honey in a small bowl.

2 Lay the Nori sheets flat on a baking tray and roast in an oven at 180°C/350F°/Gas mark 4 for 3 minutes until crisp.

3 In a large bowl, mix the Nori and rice with all the other ingredients. Just before serving, add the dressing to the salad and serve very cold with a small side dish of Japanese rice crackers.

FAT: 5G (8%) • PROTEIN: 6G (12%) • CARBOHYDRATE: 41G (14%) • FIBRE: 3G (12%)
VITAMIN C: 80% • MAGNESIUM: 33% • SODIUM: 35% • CHOLESTEROL: 0

Dandelion and Pancetta Salad

This is probably the most potent anti-cancer salad you will ever eat, and the main ingredient – dandelion leaves – could be growing for free in your garden. Packed with nutrients, this simple dish can help lower cholesterol and boost energy levels. It also improves the condition of your skin and helps your immune system to build potent antibodies.

SERVES 6 ① ③ ④ ⑤ ⑥ ⑦ ⑧ ⑨

1 small French baguette

2 tbsp olive oil

200g (7oz) pancetta (Italian bacon), cut into strips

2 tbsp balsamic vinegar

500g (1lb 2oz) fresh dandelion leaves, cleaned

80g (3oz) fresh flat-leaved parsley, chopped, to garnish

For the dressing:

100ml (3½fl oz) olive oil

4 tbsp balsamic vinegar

1 tsp wholegrain mustard

1 Combine all the ingredients to make the salad dressing.

2 Cut the baguette into bite-sized cubes and sauté in olive oil until golden brown to make croûtons. Remove from the pan and leave to drain on kitchen paper.

3 In a griddle pan, cook the pancetta over a low heat. When golden brown, splash a few drops of balsamic vinegar into the pan to caramelize and sweet-coat the meat (deglaze). Add 100g (3½oz) croûtons, stir briefly and remove from the heat.

4 Put the dandelion leaves in a large bowl, with the dressing. Add the pancetta and the croûtons. Serve with chopped parsley sprinkled over each portion.

FAT: 32G (49%) • PROTEIN: 13G (26%) • CARBOHYDRATE: 14G (5%)
FIBRE: 2G (8%) • VITAMIN A: 160% • VITAMIN B12: 34% • VITAMIN C: 60%
CHOLESTEROL: 20%

Classic Caesar Salad

The retinol (a form of vitamin A) in this dish comes from the Parmesan cheese and can enhance immunity and improve skin quality. As well as building skeletal strength, the calcium, albeit from the high-fat Parmesan, can still help lower cholesterol, provide energy and help to relieve depression.

SERVES 6 ① ③ ④ ⑤ ⑥ ⑦ ⑧

2 Cos lettuces

3 slices organic white bread

50ml (2fl oz) olive oil

12 black olives

12 anchovy fillets

50g (1¾ oz) fresh Parmesan cheese

For the dressing:

1 egg, beaten

3 garlic cloves, crushed

1 tsp soy sauce

50ml (2fl oz) olive oil

juice of 1 lemon

freshly ground black pepper

1 Wash and drain the Cos lettuces. Cut into generous-sized pieces and arrange in a large salad bowl. Cut the sliced bread into small cubes. Heat the olive oil in a saucepan and sauté the cubes gently to make croûtons.

2 To make the dressing, mix the egg with the crushed garlic and soy sauce. Drizzle in the olive oil, little by little, and whisk gently. Add the lemon juice and season to taste.

3 Add the croûtons, olives, anchovies and dressing to the Cos lettuce leaves. Toss gently to coat them all. Use a potato peeler to shave fresh Parmesan on to the top of the salad and serve with a crusty French baguette.

You can also add prawns or crisp bacon pieces to this salad.

FAT: 12G (19%) • PROTEIN: 9G (18%) • CARBOHYDRATE: 4G (1%)
FIBRE: 3G (10%) • VITAMIN A: 15% • CALCIUM: 20% • IRON: 10%
CHOLESTEROL: 6%

Wakame and Daikon Salad

A member of the radish family, daikon, which is also called mooli, is a long, white Japanese radish with a pungent, sweet flavour. The name means giant root and it accounts for a quarter of Japan's vegetable crop. In Chinese medicine, radishes are used to cleanse the liver and promote digestion. Wakame, a long, dark-green seaweed, is an excellent vegetarian source of vitamin B12.

SERVES 6 ① ② ③ ④ ⑤ ⑩

1 medium-sized daikon

3 tsp sea salt (to leech the water from the daikon; do not eat)

50g (1¾oz) dried wakame

5 tsp sesame seeds

1 small red chilli, sliced, to garnish

For the dressing:

3 tsp sugar

5 tsp rice vinegar

3 tsp Japanese soy sauce

1 Peel and cut the daikon into four pieces, lengthways, then cut each piece very thinly into delicate slices. Lay these in a colander and sprinkle the sea salt on top. Leave for 15 minutes to leech out the fluids.

2 Soak the wakame in hot water for 10 minutes. Toast the sesame seeds (without oil) until brown.

3 Rinse the daikon slices thoroughly and squeeze out the excess water. Drain the wakame and cut very thinly.

4 To make the salad dressing, mix together the sugar, vinegar and soy sauce.

5 In a salad bowl, combine the wakame, daikon and the dressing. Just before serving, sprinkle with the toasted sesame seeds and garnish with slices of fiery red chilli. For a special treat, serve this salad with prawn crackers.

FAT: 1.5G (2%) • PROTEIN: 1G (2%) • CARBOHYDRATE: 7G (2%)
FIBRE: 1G (5%) • VITAMIN C: 50% • CALCIUM: 7% • CHOLESTEROL: 0

Marinated Roasted Mixed Peppers on a Bed of Rocket

Stress depletes the body's reserves of vitamin C, so in busy periods try this salad, which is crammed with lots of healthy nutrients, especially vitamin C. This vitamin is a powerful antioxidant and an excellent detoxifier. As well as scavenging for carcinogens and other toxins, it also helps the body to absorb blood-building iron and bone-strengthening calcium.

SERVES 6

1 large red pepper

1 large green pepper

1 large orange pepper

1 large yellow pepper

1 large black (capsican) pepper

50ml (2fl oz) olive oil

400g (14oz) fresh rocket leaves

25g (1oz) fresh basil leaves, chopped, to garnish

25g (1oz) fresh sage leaves, chopped, to garnish

For the marinade:

120ml (3¾fl oz) olive oil

4 tbsp balsamic vinegar

juice of 2 lemons

5 garlic cloves, crushed

freshly ground black pepper

1 Cut all the peppers in half lengthways. Remove the stems and deseed them. Place them cut-side down in a roasting tray and brush each one with olive oil. Roast under a grill or in a very hot oven until the skins blacken. Leave to cool, peel, then cut into long, thin strips.

2 Combine all the ingredients for the marinade. Check the seasoning.

3 Add the peppers to the bowl of rocket and drizzle over the marinade. Chill for at least 3 hours in the refrigerator before garnishing with basil and sage and serving with warm foccacia bread.

FAT: 1G (5%) • PROTEIN: 3G (6%) • CARBOHYDRATE: 20G (7%) • FIBRE: 4G (16%)
VITAMIN A: 190% • VITAMIN C: 390% • CHOLESTEROL: 0

Cassoulet de la Mer

Present in every single cell in the body, phosphorous works with calcium to promote bone and heart health. You need to eat these minerals in a ratio of 2:1 in favour of calcium. This dish contains abundant supplies of both as well as vitamin C, which helps the body to absorb calcium and aids the excretion of toxic metals.

SERVES 6

300g (10½oz) dried flageolet beans

6 fresh sage leaves

freshly ground black pepper

5 strands of saffron

4 garlic cloves, crushed

1 large onion, chopped

2 fennel bulbs, chopped

50ml (2fl oz) olive oil

6 large tomatoes, skinned, deseeded and chopped

1 star anise

1 sprig of thyme

2 bay leaves

2 litres (3½ pints) fish stock

2 tbsp fresh tarragon, chopped

300g (10½oz) undyed, smoked haddock fillets

800g (1lb 12oz) sea bass fillet

12 king prawns, uncooked

1 Soak the flageolet beans for 24 hours. Boil a pan of water and cook the beans with 3 sage leaves for 1–1½ hours, or until tender. Only season at the end of the cooking time to avoid the skin of the beans toughening. Place the saffron in a little boiling water and allow to infuse.

2 Sauté the garlic, onion and fennel in the olive oil for 5 minutes, then add the chopped tomatoes, star anise, thyme, remaining sage, bay leaves, fish stock and saffron, together with the water it has been infused in.

3 Transfer the sauce to an ovenproof casserole dish, add the chopped tarragon and bring all these ingredients to the boil on the hob. Heat the oven to 160°C/325°F/Gas 3. Add the smoked haddock and sea bass to the casserole, place in the oven and cook slowly for 1 hour.

4 Add the flageolet beans and the king prawns and cook for a further 30 minutes. Season and serve with baby new potatoes.

FAT: 14G (22%) • PROTEIN: 50G (100%) • CARBOHYDRATE: 24G (8%) • FIBRE: 7G (27%)
VITAMIN A: 40% • VITAMIN C: 100% • PHOSPHOROUS: 63% • CHOLESTEROL: 32%

Roasted Sea Bass with Lentils, Leeks and a Warm Tomato Vinaigrette

No wonder they call fish brain food. Potassium, which works inside the cells to regulate heartbeat, also improves mental clarity and boosts energy levels. Lentils are high in calcium, magnesium, phosphorous, sulphur and vitamin A and are a nutritional power food: eat a moderate portion twice a week.

SERVES 6   ① ③ ④ ⑥ ⑧ ⑨

180g (6¼oz) puy lentils

700ml (1¼ pints) chicken (or vegetable) stock

freshly ground black pepper

3 leeks, white parts only, cut into julienne strips

1 tsp olive oil

90ml (3¼ fl oz) reduced-fat cream (or soya cream)

1 pinch grated nutmeg

12 x 60g (2oz) sea bass scallops (two per person)

For the vinaigrette:

100ml (3½ fl oz) olive oil

4 tbsp balsamic vinegar

4 tomatoes, skinned, deseeded and diced

2 tbsp chopped fresh chives

1 Cook the lentils in the stock for about 30 minutes, or until tender. Drain, season and put to one side.

2 Sauté the leeks gently in the olive oil until tender, but not discoloured, then add the cream. Season to taste, add the nutmeg and keep warm.

3 Season the sea bass scallops and cook them on a non-stick griddle (without oil) for 2 minutes on each side.

4 To make the tomato vinaigrette, mix the olive oil and balsamic vinegar in a small saucepan. Add the diced tomatoes and warm gently over a low heat. Add the chopped chives and season to taste.

5 To serve, arrange the leeks in the middle of six large plates. Place one scallop on top of each pile and cover with lentils. Balance the second scallop on top of the lentils and cover generously with the warm tomato vinaigrette.

You can replace the sea bass with salmon or monkfish fillets.

FAT: 20G (31%) • PROTEIN: 27G (54%) • CARBOHYDRATE: 18G (6%)
FIBRE: 4G (17%) • VITAMIN A: 30% • VITAMIN C: 60% • CALCIUM: 8%
MAGNESIUM: 29% • PHOSPHOROUS: 42% • POTASSIUM: 81% • CHOLESTEROL: 18%

Cod Fillet with Butter Bean Mash

A low-fat saltwater fish, fresh cod is enjoying a renaissance among top chefs. It provides B vitamins, including B1, which helps metabolize carbohydrates and aids digestion by increasing production of hydrochloric acid, needed to break down food in the stomach. This dish also contains sage which provides manganese, required by the body to metabolize vitamin C. Sage is also a good tonic for the lungs and the female reproductive system.

SERVES 6   ① ② ③ ⑤ ⑥ ⑦ ⑧ ⑨

400g (14oz) dried butter beans

10 fresh sage leaves

1 sprig of fresh rosemary

½ medium-sized carrot

½ medium-sized onion

100ml (3½fl oz) olive oil

5 tsp balsamic vinegar

freshly ground black pepper

6 tomatoes

1 tsp coriander seeds

1kg (2lb 4oz) cod fillet, with skin

juice of 2 lemons

1 bunch of fresh flat-leaved parsley, to garnish

1 Soak the butter beans overnight and cook in a pan of water with the sage, rosemary, carrot and onion for 1–1½ hours, or until tender. When cooked, drain and mash three-quarters of the beans with some of the cooking juice, discarding the herbs, carrot and onion.

2 Add the balsamic vinegar and 60ml (2fl oz) of the olive oil. Season to taste. Add the rest of the beans, leaving them unmashed to provide texture.

3 Cut the tomatoes in half, lengthways. Grease a baking tray with olive oil, and sprinkle over the coriander seeds and seasoning. Place the tomatoes on top and cook them very slowly, with the oven on its lowest setting, for 2 hours until soft. Then quarter them, skin them and cut the quarters in half again. Put to one side.

4 Cook the cod fillet on a non-stick griddle pan, skin-side down for 3 minutes. Season. Turn over and cook for a further 3 minutes. Season again. Splash the lemon juice into the pan to deglaze (create a caramelized sauce).

5 To serve, spoon the butter bean mash onto a large plate. Place the cod fillet on top and arrange the tomatoes around the edge. Drizzle the cooking sauce over the fish and garnish with parsley and freshly ground black pepper.

FAT: 17G (26%) • PROTEIN: 45G (90%) • CARBOHYDRATE: 18G (6%)
FIBRE: 5G (19%) • VITAMIN A: 50% • VITAMIN C: 60%
MANGANESE: 24% • CHOLESTEROL: 30%

Monkfish Scallops and Oysters with Liquorice Sauce

Zinc-rich oysters together with spinach brimming with carotenes, and vitamin A-rich carrots and beetroot, make this recipe a potent anti-cancer feast. As well as protecting against cancer of the prostate, zinc has recently been shown to be useful in the treatment of mental illness. Liquorice has an anti-viral action but can trigger water retention so avoid it if you are suffering from premenstrual syndrome (PMS).

SERVES 6 ③ ④ ⑤ ⑥ ⑦ ⑧ ⑩

200g (7oz) carrots, cut into julienne strips

200g (7oz) leeks, white parts only, cut into julienne strips

80g (3oz) olive oil spread

400g (14oz) young spinach leaves

freshly ground black pepper

6 fresh oysters

6 x 180g (6¼oz) monkfish scallops

40g (1½oz) cooked beetroot, cut into fine strips

1 small bunch of fresh chervil, chopped, to garnish

For the sauce:

3 shallots, finely diced

400ml (14fl oz) medium white wine

120ml (3¾fl oz) reduced-fat single cream

1 pinch of liquorice powder

1 Sauté the carrots and leeks in the olive oil spread over a gentle heat. Wash the spinach leaves and cook them in a saucepan with a tablespoon of water until wilted. Season and put to one side.

2 Open the oysters and strain the juices through a sieve. Keep the oyster flesh and juice, but discard the shells.

3 To make the sauce, cook the shallots in the white wine until three-quarters of the wine has evaporated. Add the juice from the oysters, the cream and the liquorice powder and reduce for 2 minutes.

4 Season the monkfish scallops and cook without oil on a non-stick griddle pan for 3 minutes on each side.

5 When you are ready to serve, poach the oysters in the liquorice sauce for 3 minutes and warm the vegetables. Place a pile of spinach in the middle of each plate. Put a monkfish scallop on top, then an oyster, followed by some leeks, carrots and beetroot. Surround the fish with the liquorice sauce and sprinkle the dish with chopped chervil leaves.

FAT: 17G (27%) • PROTEIN: 33G (66%) • CARBOHYDRATE: 14G (5%)
FIBRE: 4G (14%) • VITAMIN A: 250% • MANGANESE: 57% • POTASSIUM: 148%
ZINC: 64% • CHOLESTEROL: 34%

Chilli Crab Cakes Singapore-style

Copper deficiency can contribute to osteoporosis. Combat brittle bones with this dish that contains copper-rich crab meat. Crab also provides vitamin B3 (niacin), which can help reduce cholesterol, boost energy levels and give you healthier-looking skin.

SERVES 6 ② ③ ④ ⑤ ⑥ ⑨ ⑩

1.2kg (2lb 11oz) potatoes, cut into chunks

3 fresh red chillies, deseeded and diced

4 dried chillies, chopped

2 tsp shrimp paste

1 lemon grass stalk, roughly chopped

10 unsalted cashew nuts

600g (1lb 5oz) crab meat

100g (3½oz) flour (use wheat-free if intolerant)

3 eggs, beaten

150g (5½oz) breadcrumbs

50ml (2fl oz) sesame oil, for frying

2 tbsp chopped coriander

For the sauce:

2 tsp sesame oil, to sauté

2 shallots, chopped

4 garlic cloves, crushed

2.5cm (1in) fresh root ginger, grated

500ml (17fl oz) chicken stock

1 Cook the potatoes in boiling water for 15–20 minutes until soft. Mash and put to one side. In a food processor, mix together all the chillies, the shrimp paste, lemon grass and cashew nuts to form a smooth paste.

2 Combine the crab meat with the mashed potatoes and one-third of the paste. Divide this mixture into 12 round-shaped cakes. Coat each of these first with flour, then beaten egg followed by breadcrumbs. Put to one side.

3 For the sauce, sauté the shallots, crushed garlic and grated ginger in sesame oil for a few minutes. Add the remaining two-thirds of the chilli and nut paste and cook for a few more minutes. Add the chicken stock and cook for another 2–3 minutes until the sauce has thickened.

4 Heat a shallow pool of sesame oil and add the crab cakes. Cook over a medium heat until golden brown on both sides (about 5 minutes per side).

5 Pour the sauce onto six dinner plates and place two crab cakes in the middle of each, propped up against each other. Garnish with chopped coriander leaves.

To serve as a starter, reduce to one crab cake per person. For a quick supper, replace the sauce with a squeeze of lime juice.

FAT: 23G (35%) • PROTEIN: 36G (72%) • CARBOHYDRATE: 79G (26%)
FIBRE: 5G (21%) • VITAMIN B3: 70% • VITAMIN C: 100% • COPPER: 39% • IRON: 30%
CHOLESTEROL: 59%

Carri of Tuna and Ginger

The amount of potassium that you need, which in this dish comes from fish and vegetables, depends on how much muscle you have and your state of health, since low blood-sugar and severe stomach upsets can deplete the body's stores. Inspired by Mauritian cuisine, this recipe is ideal for people convalescing from illness and those who are very fit.

SERVES 6 ① ③ ④ ⑧

60ml (2fl oz) olive oil

3 large onions, sliced

6 garlic cloves, crushed

3cm (1¼in) fresh root ginger, grated

60ml (2fl oz) olive oil

1 pinch of ground cumin

1.3kg (2lb 14½oz) fresh tuna, diced

1kg (2lb 4oz) tomatoes, skinned and roughly chopped

5 tsp Thai fish sauce

1 litre (1¾ pints) fish stock

freshly ground black pepper

1 bunch of spring onions, chopped

1 To make a compote, heat half the olive oil in a large heavy-based saucepan. Cook the onion, garlic and ginger until soft. Add the ground cumin and a little water and cook for 20 minutes until tender and slightly browned.
2 Seal the tuna in the remaining olive oil and transfer to the compote. Add the tomatoes, Thai fish sauce and fish stock. Season and leave to cook very slowly for 30–40 minutes.
3 Check the seasoning again and, just before you serve, add the chopped spring onion. Serve with rice.

This dish is even more delicious when re-heated the following day when the flavours have had time to seep through all the ingredients. You can also make a Carri in exactly the same way with meat.

FAT: 19g (29%) • PROTEIN: 54g (108%) • CARBOHYDRATE: 18g (6%)
FIBRE: 4g (16%) • VITAMIN A: 120% • VITAMIN C: 90% • POTASSIUM: 125%
CHOLESTEROL: 27%

Salmon Fillet with Grilled Hazelnuts

This dish is packed with protein and the antioxidant vitamins A and C, and the hazelnuts contain manganese, which provides additional antioxidant, anti-cancer protection and helps to keep the brain, skeleton, circulation, and immune and nervous systems in good health. Low manganese levels are associated with atherosclerosis.

SERVES 6 ① ④ ⑤ ⑦ ⑧ ⑩

1 small cauliflower head, cut into florets

1 pinch of nutmeg

2 tbsp soya cream

freshly ground black pepper

125g (4½oz) hazelnuts

100ml (3½fl oz) hazelnut or olive oil

6 x 180g (6¼oz) salmon fillets, with the skin on

5 tsp balsamic vinegar

1 tbsp chopped fresh chives, to garnish

1 Cook the cauliflower in boiling water until soft. Drain and transfer to a food processor. Blend with the nutmeg and soya cream to form a mousse. Season.
2 Place the hazelnuts in a roasting tin and bake them in a hot oven for 15 minutes until the skin slips off easily. Roughly crush them and warm them gently in a small saucepan with the hazelnut oil. Do not boil. Remove the nuts from the pan, reserving the oil.
3 Season the salmon fillets and cook, skin-side down on a non-stick griddle pan (no oil is necessary) for 3 minutes. Turn and cook for another 3 minutes. Keep warm.
4 To serve, place each salmon fillet on a warm plate with the hazelnuts. Drizzle some of the oil you cooked the nuts in over the fish and nuts. Splash with balsamic vinegar. To one side of the fish, add some cauliflower mousse and sprinkle chopped chives over the entire dish.

FAT: 50g (76%) • PROTEIN: 45g (90%) • CARBOHYDRATE: 20g (7%)
FIBRE: 9g (35%) • VITAMIN A: 90% • VITAMIN C: 150% • MANGANESE: 28%
CHOLESTEROL: 36%

Bouillabaisse

This tasty, classic fish stew is a storehouse of B vitamins and heart-protecting folic acid. It also provides more than a day's full requirement of manganese, needed for the manufacture of vitamin K, which promotes healthy blood clotting.

SERVES 6

3 large onions, chopped

3 leeks, white parts only, chopped

3 stalks of celery, chopped

6 garlic cloves, chopped

1 large fennel bulb, chopped

120ml (3¾fl oz) olive oil

25g (1oz) orange peel

4 large tomatoes, skinned, deseeded and chopped

1 tsp saffron powder

1 tsp fresh thyme

3 bay leaves

1 litre (1¾ pints) water

300g (10½oz) conger eel

300g (10½oz) monkfish

300g (10½oz) skate wings

4 tsp Pernod

3 small red mullets

300g (10½oz) Arctic sea bass

300g (10½oz) cod

500g (1lb 2oz) fresh mussels, cleaned

8 langoustines (with their shells)

1 pinch of cayenne pepper

For the croûtons:

16 slices of French baguette

3 garlic cloves

For the rouille:

6 slices French bread, cubed, soaked in milk

6 garlic cloves, crushed

1 pinch of cayenne pepper

1 pinch of saffron powder

200ml (7fl oz) olive oil

1 To make the croûtons, grill the slices of dry French bread on both sides and rub them with fresh garlic.

2 For the rouille, blend the garlic with the cayenne pepper and saffron to form a smooth paste. Season. Squeeze and drain the French bread you have presoaked in milk and blend with the garlic paste. Add the olive oil, little by little, blending as you go. Check the seasoning.

3 To make the bouillabaisse, cook the vegetables in olive oil, until tender. Add the orange peel, tomatoes, herbs and water. Bring to the boil, then simmer for 25 minutes.

4 Put the Conger eel, monkfish and skate in the pot with the boiling vegetables. Add the Pernod and cook for another 5 minutes. Add the rest of the fish and cook for another 7 minutes.

5 Finally, add the mussels and the langoustines, and cook for 3–5 minutes. Strain the fish and vegetables and arrange in a large, warmed serving dish.

6 Reduce the sauce by boiling rapidly for 10 minutes. Check the seasoning and pour over the fish and vegetables. Serve with the croûtons and the rouille. You can spread the rouille on the croûtons or drop a dollop into the fish dish.

FAT: 44G (67%) • PROTEIN: 51G (102%) • CARBOHYDRATE: 28G (9%) • FIBRE: 3G (13%)
VITAMIN C: 50% • MANGANESE: 186% • IRON: 35% • CHOLESTEROL: 39%

POULTRY

Honeyed Chicken with Passion Fruit

Poultry is an excellent source of protein – and full of flavour if you buy organic. It is rich in the B-complex vitamins, especially cholesterol-lowering B3 (niacin), which also promotes healthy digestion and glowing skin, as well as boosting energy levels. The honey and the vitamin C will increase your resistance to disease. Finally, the potassium-packed passion fruit can help maintain a healthy heart.

SERVES 6

80g (3oz) passion fruit pulp

6 organic chicken breasts, skinless

60ml (2fl oz) olive oil

juice of 3 lemons

2 tsp ground cinnamon

60g (2oz) honey

20g (¾oz) fresh root ginger, grated

freshly ground black pepper

300g (10½oz) rocket leaves

1 To pulp the passion fruits, cut them in half and scoop out the flesh. Mix together the olive oil, lemon juice, cinnamon, honey and ginger to form a marinade. Coat the chicken breasts in the marinade. Season, and chill for 2 hours.

2 Drain the marinade from the chicken and cook the meat on a griddle pan, over a high heat, for 2 minutes on each side.

3 Put the chicken breasts on a baking tray, cover with the passion fruit pulp and finish cooking in a preheated oven (190°C/375°F/Gas 5) for 8 minutes. Serve on a bed of rocket leaves, which provide plenty of iron and vitamins.

FAT: 16G (25%) • PROTEIN: 59G (118%) • CARBOHYDRATE: 20G (7%) • FIBRE: 4G (16%)
VITAMIN A: 140% • VITAMIN B3: 216% • VITAMIN C: 40% • IRON: 25% • POTASSIUM: 81% • CHOLESTEROL: 52%

Chicken Jambalaya

The best known of the carotenoids is betacarotene. The body converts this to vitamin A, which is vital for new cell growth. It can also improve skin condition, especially in cases of acne, and can help slow the ageing process. So if you want to look as young as you feel, then this recipe, with its Spanish origins and high betacarotene content, is the dish for you. Its high potassium levels will help to reduce blood pressure and counter the high-fat content of the chorizo sausage.

SERVES 6   ① ③ ❹ ❻ ❽

60ml (2fl oz) olive oil

1 large onion, diced

6 garlic cloves, chopped

1 green pepper, diced

2 red chillies, deseeded and chopped

100g (3½oz) celery chopped

250g (9oz) smoked chorizo sausage, sliced

1kg (2lb 4oz) chicken pieces, boneless and skinless

2 bay leaves

2 sprigs of fresh thyme, chopped

1 generous pinch of Spanish cayenne pepper

freshly ground black pepper

500g (1lb 2oz) white rice

1.2 litres (2 pints) chicken stock

250g (9oz) tomatoes, chopped

3 tbsp chopped fresh parsley

1 Heat the olive oil in a large, flat-bottomed pan. Cook the onion, garlic, green pepper, red chillies, celery and chorizo for 5 minutes. Add the chicken pieces, bay leaves, thyme, cayenne pepper and seasoning.

2 Cook until all the chicken pieces are beginning to brown, then add the rice and stir for 2 minutes until all the grains are thoroughly coated.

3 Pour in the chicken stock and add the tomatoes and fresh parsley. Cook for 20 minutes until all the liquid has been completely absorbed. Serve with brown rice and a salad.

FAT: 41G (63%) • PROTEIN: 56G (112%) • CARBOHYDRATE: 34G (11%)
FIBRE: 2G (10%) • VITAMIN A: 50% • VITAMIN C: 140% • POTASSIUM: 91%
CHOLESTEROL: 62%

Turkey and Green Bean Stir-fry

The turkey in this dish is a low-fat option and provides vitamin D – the sunshine vitamin – which enables the body to use both calcium and phosphorous properly to make strong bones and teeth. The roasted sesame seeds provide vitamin B3 (thiamine), which keeps the heart and muscles functioning and helps to lift the spirits.

SERVES 6   ❹ ⑤ ❼ ❽ ❾

2 tbsp sesame oil

400g (14oz) turkey breasts, skinless and cut widthways into thin strips

100g (3½oz) oyster mushrooms, sliced

150g (5½oz) fresh bamboo shoots, diced

3 medium-sized carrots, thinly sliced diagonally

80ml (3fl oz) chicken stock

60ml (2fl oz) Japanese soy sauce

125g (4oz) fresh green beans, sliced diagonally

25g (1oz) sesame seeds, toasted

1 Heat the sesame oil in a wok and stir-fry the turkey strips for 2 minutes. Add the mushrooms, bamboo shoots and carrots and cook for 3 minutes. Add the stock and soy sauce and cook for a further 20 minutes, until the carrots are tender but still firm.

2 Add the sliced green beans and roasted sesame seeds and cook for 5 more minutes, stirring continuously. Serve with fragrant white rice.

For variety, use sprouts, peas or courgettes instead of the green beans.

FAT: 8G (12%) • PROTEIN: 24G (48%) • CARBOHYDRATE: 7G (2%)
FIBRE: 3G (11%) • VITAMIN A: 140% • VITAMIN B3: 51% • VITAMIN D: 4%
IRON: 15% • POTASSIUM: 50% • CHOLESTEROL: 18%

Chicken Kuroke (Japanese-style Chicken Cakes)

The vitamin D in this recipe comes, surprisingly, from the immunity-boosting Japanese shiitake mushrooms, which have a proven anti-viral action. They stop viruses from dividing and are thus said to protect against flu. They are traditionally eaten to reduce fatigue and lower blood pressure, slow ageing and prevent ulcers.

SERVES 6 ❶ ❹ ❻ ❽ ❾ ❿

100g (3½oz) fresh (or dried and rehydrated) shiitake mushrooms, sliced	2 tbsp Japanese soy sauce
1 garlic clove, sliced	350g (12oz) mashed potatoes
75g (2¾oz) spring onion, chopped	250g (9oz) leftover cooked chicken meat, finely chopped
75ml (2½fl oz) olive oil	100g (3½oz) breadcrumbs
2 medium-sized fresh eggs, beaten	50g (1¾oz) roasted nori, crushed

1 Sauté the mushrooms, garlic and spring onion in 4 teaspoonfuls of the olive oil for 3 minutes. Leave to cool.

2 In a large bowl, combine the mushroom mixture with the eggs, soy sauce, mashed potatoes and chicken meat. From this mix, form even-sized balls and flatten them to shape eight small cakes.

3 Mix the breadcrumbs with the crushed nori and roll the chicken cakes in this mixture. Cook them in a shallow pool of the remaining olive oil for about 5 minutes until they are golden and the centres are heated through. Serve on salad with a little soy sauce.

FAT: 13G (20%) • PROTEIN: 29G (58%) • CARBOHYDRATE: 42G (14%)
FIBRE: 3G (13%) • VITAMIN D: 52% • CALCIUM: 15% • IRON: 20% • CHOLESTEROL: 74%

Spiedini di Pollo

This dish has a great name and wonderful health benefits. Surveys have found a direct relationship between selenium levels and cancer rates – the higher the former, the lower the latter. The Cancer Institute in the United States reckons that a protective daily dose of 200mcg of selenium could eventually see a 70 per cent drop in rates of all cancers. Bread was always an excellent source of selenium, but thanks to over-refining, most varieties no longer contain it, with the result that much of the population is now deficient in this important antioxidant mineral.

SERVES 4 ❸ ❹ ❽ ❿

4 chicken breasts, skinless	16 baby white onions, peeled
juice of 3 lemons	
60ml (2fl oz) olive oil	24 large fresh sage leaves
1 pinch of cayenne pepper	24 slices of smoked pancetta
2 bay leaves	16 lemon wedges
1 sprig of fresh thyme, chopped	(you will also need 8 metal skewers for cooking)

1 Cut each chicken breast into six pieces. Combine the lemon juice, olive oil, cayenne pepper, bay leaves, thyme and whole onions in a bowl to make a marinade. Add the pieces of meat and leave to chill in the refrigerator for 3–4 hours.

2 Remove the chicken from the marinade, reserving the onions for later. Roll a large sage leaf around each piece of marinated chicken. Then carefully wrap each bundle in a slice of pancetta.

3 On a skewer, thread a lemon wedge, skin first, followed by a baby onion, three chicken and pancetta bundles, another baby onion and a last lemon wedge, flesh first. Do the same for the remaining seven skewers.

4 To cook, grill or barbecue for 20–25 minutes, turning frequently. Serve two skewers per person with salad or pasta.

FAT: 22G (34%) • PROTEIN: 48G (96%) • CARBOHYDRATE: 23G (8%)
FIBRE: 8G (31%) • CALCIUM: 30% • IRON: 35% • SELENIUM: 20% • CHOLESTEROL: 41%

Chicken Marengo

Chicken is a rich source of magnesium, which is known as the anti-stress mineral. It converts blood sugar into energy and plays a vital role in nerve and muscle function. It can also help fight depression, protect against heart attacks, aid digestion and keep tooth enamel safe from decay. Heavy drinking lowers levels of this mineral in the body.

SERVES 6 ② ④ ⑤ ⑥ ⑦ ⑨ ⑩

60ml (2fl oz) olive oil

freshly ground black pepper

1 large whole chicken (about 2.7kg/6lb), cut into 8 pieces and skinned

1 large onion, chopped

5 garlic cloves, crushed

400g (14oz) button mushrooms, sliced

250g (9oz) tomatoes, skinned, deseeded and chopped

120ml (3¾fl oz) white wine

1 sprig of fresh thyme

1 bay leaf

2 tbsp fresh flat-leaved parsley, chopped, to garnish

1 Heat the olive oil in a large, heavy-based pan. Season the chicken pieces and cook until brown. Remove the meat and put to one side.

2 Cook the onion and garlic in the chicken juices, until they soften. Then add the mushrooms, tomatoes, wine, thyme and bay leaves.

3 Return the chicken pieces to the pan, cover and cook for 1 hour over a low heat. Sprinkle with the chopped parsley before serving.

FAT: 29G (44%) • PROTEIN: 143G (286%) • CARBOHYDRATE: 10G (3%) • FIBRE: 3G (11%)
VITAMIN C: 45% • MAGNESIUM: 48% • IRON: 40% • CHOLESTEROL: 129%

Chicken Provençale

This recipe contains the three big powerful antioxidant vitamins A, C and E. The vitamins A and C come from the red peppers. Vitamin E, which enhances the activity of both vitamins A and C, is provided by the olive oil. Unlike other fat-soluble vitamins, vitamin E – which repairs tissue and reduces blood pressure – is stored in the body for only a short time, so it is important to eat it every day.

SERVES 6 ① ④ ⑥ ⑧ ⑨

1.5kg (3lb 6oz) chicken legs and thighs, skinless

90ml (3fl oz) olive oil

2 large onions, chopped

5 garlic cloves, chopped

3 large shallots, chopped

500g (1lb 2oz) red peppers, cut into thick strips

500g (1lb 2oz) tomatoes, chopped

100ml (3½fl oz) white wine

1 sprig of fresh oregano

1 sprig of fresh thyme

2 bay leaves, crushed

1 pinch of cayenne pepper

freshly ground black pepper

150g (5½oz) pitted green olives

100g (3½oz) pitted black olives

5 fresh basil leaves, chopped

1 Brown the chicken pieces in olive oil for 5 minutes, remove from the pan and put to one side.

2 In the same saucepan, gently cook the onions, garlic and shallots until tender. Then add the red pepper strips, chopped tomatoes, wine, oregano, thyme, bay leaves and cayenne pepper.

3 Next, return the chicken pieces to the pan. Season, cover and cook very slowly for 1 hour over a low heat.

4 Add the olives and cook for another 20 minutes before sprinkling with chopped fresh basil and serving hot with rice or fresh pasta.

FAT: 39G (60%) • PROTEIN: 55G (110%) • CARBOHYDRATE: 23G (8%)
FIBRE: 4G (16%) • VITAMIN A: 80% • VITAMIN C: 270% • VITAMIN E: 34%
CHOLESTEROL: 61%

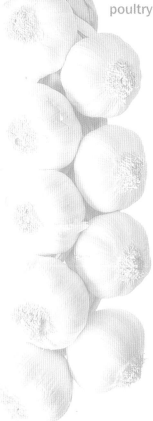

Chicken Moorg

The B vitamins work better in combination than they do alone and poultry combined with brown rice provide most of them. The chicken contains vitamin B3 (niacin), which can help to lower cholesterol and blood pressure, regulate sex hormones and improve skin condition; vitamin B6, which is believed to play a role in the synthesis of anti-ageing nucleic acids; and vitamin B12, which is known as the red vitamin because it helps to build healthy blood.

SERVES 6   ② ③ ④ ⑥ ⑩

1 large onion, chopped

6 garlic cloves, chopped

2.5cm (1in) fresh ginger root, grated

juice of 2 lemons

6 chicken legs, skinned

3 chicken breasts, skinned

¼ tsp ground cinnamon

¼ tsp freshly grated nutmeg

¼ tsp cloves

¼ tsp mace

1 tsp ground cumin

1 tsp ground turmeric

1 tsp ground coriander

¼ tsp cayenne pepper

90ml (3fl oz) olive oil

250g (9oz) low-fat natural yogurt

2 tbsp fresh coriander, chopped, to garnish

For the brown pilau rice:

1 large onion

4 tsp olive oil

1 piece of cinnamon stick

450g (1lb) brown rice

1 litre (1¾ pints) vegetable stock

1 Put the chopped onion, garlic, ginger and lemon juice in a food processor and blend to a very smooth paste. Add the dry spices, olive oil and yogurt. These then form the marinade.

2 Slash the legs and the breast of the chicken pieces and place them in a large bowl. Rub the marinade over the chicken pieces, cover and leave them to rest in the refrigerator for 24 hours.

3 Wrap the chicken and marinade in foil and cook on a baking tray for 1½ hours in a preheated oven (200°C/400°F/Gas 6). Baste the meat with the marinade during cooking.

4 To make the brown pilau rice, sweat the onion in the olive oil with the cinnamon stick for 5–6 minutes until translucent. Add the rice and stir for 2 minutes to coat every grain.

5 Pour in the vegetable stock, then bring the mixture to the boil. Tip into an ovenproof casserole dish, cover and cook in a preheated oven (180°C/350°F/Gas 4) for 25–30 minutes. Garnish the chicken with fresh coriander and serve with the pilau rice.

FAT: 11G (16%) • PROTEIN: 46G (92%) • CARBOHYDRATE: 28G (9%) • FIBRE: 3G (11%)
VITAMIN B3: 135% • VITAMIN B6: 58% • VITAMIN B12: 23% • CHOLESTEROL: 41%

MEAT

Tajine

The apricots in this delicious, protein-rich North African stew are an outstanding source of both iron and betacarotene, which the body converts to vitamin A. Everyone knows that you need iron to make red blood cells, but it is less well known that women, who in one month lose almost twice as much iron as men, are frequently borderline anaemic. This dish will prevent this.

SERVES 6   ③ ④ ⑥

3 large onions, chopped

800g (1lb 12oz) pork (shoulder), diced

800g (1lb 12oz) lamb (middle neck), diced

60ml (2fl oz) olive oil

20g (¾oz) cumin seeds

35g (1¼oz) coriander seeds

1 cinnamon stick

1 pinch of cayenne pepper

1 litre (1¾ pints) chicken stock

6 carrots, sliced

juice of two lemons

80g (3oz) blanched almonds

8 dried apricots

4 tsp honey

1 tbsp fresh coriander, roughly chopped, to garnish

1 Put the chopped onions, diced meats, oil, cumin, coriander seeds, cinnamon stick and cayenne pepper in an ovenproof dish with a lid. Cover with chicken stock (or water) and cook, covered, in a preheated oven (190°C/375°F/Gas 5) for 2 hours.

2 Add the sliced carrots, lemon juice, blanched almonds and dried apricots and return to the oven for another 1½ hours.

3 Uncover the tajine, stir the honey into the cooking juices and return to the oven to cook until the sauce has thickened (about 20 minutes). Serve very hot in its cooking pot, garnished with some roughly chopped coriander.

You can make tajine with lamb, pork or beef if you prefer. It is delicious served with couscous, another traditional North African dish.

FAT: 51G (79%) • PROTEIN: 64G (128%) • CARBOHYDRATE: 23G (8%) • FIBRE: 7G (29%)
VITAMIN A: 270% • IRON: 45% • MAGNESIUM: 47% • CHOLESTEROL: 72%

Fillet of Pork with Prunes

Pork and prunes are a delicious taste combination. What's more, this is a very healthy dish. The prunes contain potassium, which promotes the efficient disposal of the body's waste products and is needed in large quantities by people with diabetes, high blood pressure and liver disease. Pork is rich in vitamin B3 (niacin), which is always depleted by stress, illness or surgery.

SERVES 6   ① ② ③ **④**

18 prunes

1kg (2lb 4oz) pork fillet

90g (3oz) walnuts

90g (3oz) almonds

90g (3oz) hazelnuts

100g (3½oz) honey

60ml (2fl oz) cider vinegar

300ml (½ pint) chicken stock

freshly ground black pepper

50g (1¾oz) white flour (for coating the pork)

50ml (2fl oz) olive oil

1 bunch of fresh chives, chopped, to garnish

1 Soak the prunes in water for 8 hours. Trim the pork fillets and cut, widthways, into 2.5cm (1in) discs. Gently crush the nuts. Drain the prunes and cut them in half.
2 In a saucepan, heat the honey until it turns to a caramel colour. Add the vinegar with the chicken stock. Season and reduce the sauce until it becomes syrupy and coats the back of the spoon. Complete the sauce by adding the nuts and the prunes. Put to one side.
3 Coat each piece of pork in flour and cook in hot olive oil until golden brown on both sides. Allow 4 minutes cooking time on each side. Season and serve. Present the pork covered with the prune sauce and garnished with chopped chives. Serve with a selection of vegetables.

FAT: 51G (79%) • PROTEIN: 41G (82%) • CARBOHYDRATE: 44G (15%)
FIBRE: 6G (24%) • VITAMIN B3: 79% • VITAMIN E: 59%
POTASSIUM: 117% • CHOLESTEROL: 35%

Pork with Tofu and Vegetables

This recipe provides 71.44mg of vitamin C per serving – the intake for optimum health is between 60 and 100mcg. In mega doses – around 5,000mg a day – vitamin C becomes a medicine that has been shown to lengthen life expectancy of patients diagnosed with terminal cancer. Tofu is an amazing food that contains powerful phytochemicals, which many now believe can actually reverse diseases, including cancers and heart disease.

SERVES 6   ① **④ ⑤ ⑥ ⑧ ⑨**

750g (1lb 11oz) lean pork, cut into 2.5cm (1in) cubes

2 celery stalks, cut into 2.5cm (1in) lengths

100g (3½oz) bamboo shoots, sliced

1 large onion, sliced in rings

200g (7oz) tofu, cut into 2.5cm (1in) cubes

1 Chinese cabbage, chopped into squares

100g (3½oz) spinach leaves

For the Oriental-style sauce:

100ml (3½fl oz) soy sauce

juice of 2 lemons

4 tsp rice vinegar

20g (¾oz) fresh root ginger, grated

1 spring onion, chopped

1 Place the pork in a pan and cover with water. Cook for 40 minutes, skimming the top while cooking. Add the celery, sliced bamboo shoots, onion slices, tofu, cabbage and spinach to the pork and cook for another 20–30 minutes.
2 Combine all the ingredients for the sauce in a small bowl and mix together well.
3 Bring the pork with its stock and the vegetables direct to the table in a large pot. Serve with white rice and the Oriental-style sauce.

FAT: 17G (27%) • PROTEIN: 32G (64%) • CARBOHYDRATE: 8G (3%)
FIBRE: 3G (11%) • VITAMIN A: 100% • VITAMIN C: 120% • FOLIC ACID: 35%
CHOLESTEROL: 26%

Nepalese Pork Curry

Vitamin C is a multi-role nutrient – it improves the body's ability to absorb other vitamins and minerals, especially calcium and iron, and helps flush out toxic metals such as mercury and lead. In this dish, the high levels come from the red pepper. However, vitamin C does not stay in the body for long – eat it at breakfast and it is gone from the body by noon. Most meat dishes are high in saturated fats, which can increase cholesterol levels. Thanks to the trimmed pork, this dish is one of the healthier meat options.

SERVES 6 ❷ ❸ ❹ ❺ ❽ ❿

800g (1lb 12 oz) boneless pork

3 onions, finely chopped

5 garlic cloves, finely chopped

60ml (2fl oz) olive oil

1 tsp ground coriander

1 tsp ground cumin

½ tsp chilli powder

1 green pepper, sliced

1 red pepper, sliced

250ml (9fl oz) water

200g (7oz) natural yogurt

freshly ground black pepper

50g (1¾oz) fresh chives, chopped

1 Trim the fat from the pork and cut into average-sized pieces. In an oven-proof casserole dish, cook the onion and garlic in the olive oil for 5 minutes, stirring constantly.
2 Add the coriander, cumin and chilli and cook for another 2 minutes. Now add the pork pieces and stir until they are coated with the spices. Add the sliced peppers, water and yogurt. Season to taste.
3 Bring to the boil on the hob and then cook in a preheated oven (180°C/350°F/Gas 4) for 1½ hours, until the meat is tender. Sprinkle with the chopped chives and serve with nutty Italian brown rice.

FAT: 26G (40%) • PROTEIN: 29G (58%) • CARBOHYDRATE: 11G (4%)
FIBRE: 3G (10%) • VITAMIN A: 45% • VITAMIN B3: 55% • VITAMIN C: 140%
CHOLESTEROL: 29%

Thai Green Beef Curry

If you eat meat, enjoy this high-fat dish as an occasional treat. Although it is higher in saturated fats (33g per portion) than any other recipe in this book, most of the fat comes from the coconut milk, rather than from the beef. As well as imparting the traditional Thai flavour, coconut milk is packed with nutrients: it provides more carbohydrate, fibre, vitamin E, folic acid, calcium, copper, selenium, magnesium and manganese than any other single ingredient in this dish.

SERVES 4 ❷ ❸ ❹ ❻ ❽ ❿

600g (1lb 5oz) best lean beef fillet, cut into strips

500ml (17fl oz) coconut milk

1 red chilli, deseeded and chopped

4cm (1½in) fresh root ginger, grated

3 kaffir lime leaves

2 tbsp Thai fish sauce

1 tbsp brown sugar

3 tbsp sesame oil, to fry

For the green curry paste:

1 fresh green chilli

20g (¾oz) fresh coriander

1 onion, diced

1 tbsp sesame oil

½ tsp ground turmeric

½ tsp shrimp paste

1 garlic clove, crushed

1 lemon grass stalk, roughly chopped

½ tsp ground cumin

½ tsp caraway seeds

1 To make the green curry paste, blend all the ingredients in a food processor to form a smooth paste. Heat the oil in a wok and cook this paste for 1 minute.
2 Add the beef strips to the paste and stir-fry for 1 minute. Add the coconut milk, chilli, ginger, kaffir lime leaves, fish sauce and brown sugar. Bring to the boil, stirring all the time. Cook for 8 minutes. Serve with white rice and noodles.

FAT: 49G (76%) • PROTEIN: 50G (100%) • CARBOHYDRATE: 15G (5%)
FIBRE: 4G (16%) • VITAMIN B3: 140% • VITAMIN C: 100% • VITAMIN E: 140%
CALCIUM: 10% • COPPER: 35% • FOLIC ACID: 10% • IRON: 50% • MAGNESIUM: 36%
MANGANESE: 53% • SELENIUM: 21% • CHOLESTEROL: 165%

Steak Teriyaki

One of the symptoms of vitamin B12 deficiency is extreme fatigue. If you are vegetarian, or are on a diet that excludes eggs and dairy products, you run the risk of this deficiency, which can take up to five years for the symptoms to manifest themselves. This recipe is an effective rejuvenator because it combines meat, a rich source of vitamin B12, and sesame seeds, full of folic acid, which will give you a boost when you are feeling run down.

SERVES 4   ❷ ❸ ❹ ❻

4 x 180g (6¼oz) beef fillet steaks

125g (4oz) wholemeal noodles

4 tsp olive oil

25g (1oz) sesame seeds, roasted

For the marinade:

100ml (3½fl oz) Japanese soy sauce

4 tsp sugar

8 tsp sake

2 garlic cloves, crushed

2.5cm (1in) fresh root ginger, grated

1 Combine all the marinade ingredients in a bowl. Add the steaks and leave in the refrigerator to chill for at least 3 hours, turning the meat frequently.

2 Drain the fillets, reserving the marinade, and cook them on both sides on a non-stick griddle pan. Baste the meat with the marinade while cooking and, when done, put to one side.

3 Cook the noodles in boiling water for 3 minutes. Drain and toss with olive oil and sesame seeds. Slice the beef into very thin slices and serve with the noodles.

FAT: 27G (41%) • PROTEIN: 59G (118%) • CARBOHYDRATE: 26G (9%)
FIBRE: 3G (12%) • VITAMIN B12: 92% • FOLIC ACID: 6% • IRON: 45%
POTASSIUM: 99% • CHOLESTEROL: 50%

Costoletie d'Agnello al Parmigiano

Succulent spring lamb is an excellent source of phosphorous, the second most abundant mineral in the body. Most of it is in the bones and teeth where, together with calcium and fluoride, it makes the tissues hard. It is crucial to the formation of phospholipids, which regulate what goes in and out of cells and which are vital to both the release and storage of energy.

SERVES 4   ❸ ❺ ❻

2 racks of lamb, trimmed

60ml (2fl oz) olive oil

2 bay leaves

3 sprigs of fresh rosemary

1 sprig of fresh thyme

For the Parmesan crust:

10 black olives, pitted

10 fresh sage leaves

100g (3½oz) fresh Parmesan, grated

60ml (2fl oz) olive oil

5 garlic cloves, crushed

1 To make the Parmesan crust, put all the ingredients in a food processor and blend for 1 minute.

2 Seal the racks of lamb by frying them quickly over a high heat in olive oil, with the bay leaves, rosemary and thyme, until they have browned all over.

3 Place the meat in an ovenproof dish and cover with the Parmesan crust paste. Cook in a preheated oven (180°C/350°F/Gas 4) for 20 minutes. When the meat is cooked, cover and leave to rest for 15 minutes. Cut the chops and serve with Swiss Chard – Two Ways *(see page 106)*.

FAT: 59G (91%) • PROTEIN: 63G (126%) • CARBOHYDRATE: 4G (1%)
FIBRE: 0.56G (2%) • CALCIUM: 40% • PHOSPHOROUS: 75% • SELENIUM: 118%
CHOLESTEROL: 65%

Beef Kebab with Moroccan Sauce and Bulgar Wheat

If you love meat, hate vegetables and can't be bothered to spend hours in the kitchen cooking, this is the dish for you. Not least because you can cook it outdoors. Rich in all the B vitamins, potassium and zinc from the meat, it is also packed with fibre from the bulgar wheat, polyunsaturated fat from the pine nuts, and vitamins A and C from the red onions, chillies and tomatoes.

SERVES 6　　　　　　　　　　　　　②④⑥⑧⑨⑩

2 red onions, finely diced

3 red chillies, deseeded and finely diced

3 tbsp chopped fresh mint

1 tsp chopped fresh thyme

4 tsp olive oil

15g (½oz) ground cumin

2.5cm (1in) fresh root ginger, grated

½ tsp Tabasco sauce

freshly ground black pepper

200g (7oz) bulgar wheat

500ml (18fl oz) chicken stock

3 tbsp chopped fresh flat-leaved parsley

1kg (2lb 4oz) lean beef, minced

1 white onion, finely diced

For the Moroccan sauce:

1 small onion, diced

5 tsp olive oil

300g (10½oz) tomatoes, skinned, deseeded and chopped

15g (½oz) ground cumin

50g (1¾oz) pine kernels, roasted

80g (3oz) raisins

(you will also need 6 kebab skewers)

1 Put the red onion and chillies in a bowl with the fresh mint, thyme, olive oil, cumin, ginger and Tabasco sauce, reserving a little of the mint for garnish. Season, mix well and leave to chill for at least 2 hours in the refrigerator.

2 Meanwhile, put the bulgar wheat in a large saucepan. Add the chicken stock and diced white onion, season, and cook until the wheat has absorbed all the stock. When cooked, add the chopped parsley and put to one side.

3 To make the Moroccan sauce, cook the onion in olive oil, until tender. Add the tomatoes, cumin, pine kernels and raisins. Season and leave to cook gently over a low heat for 20 minutes.

4 To make the kebabs, roll the meat around the skewer, making a long sausage shape from one end to the other. Grill or barbecue for 6–8 minutes, turning all the time to ensure even cooking.

5 Serve the beef kebabs on a bed of herbed bulgar wheat, surrounded by the sauce and garnished with a sprinkle of fresh mint.

As a variation, serve the kebabs with couscous or rice.

FAT: 41G (64%) • PROTEIN: 41G (82%) • CARBOHYDRATE: 49G (16%) • FIBRE: 8G (33%) • VITAMIN A: 70%
VITAMIN B12: 110% • VITAMIN C: 140% • IRON: 60% • POTASSIUM: 130% • ZINC: 58% • CHOLESTEROL: 0

Gratinée of Pumpkin in its Shell

Crammed with goodness, this is practically the perfect healthy dish. Several of its nutrients either reach or surpass the minimum recommended daily amounts and its high levels of vitamins A and C pack a powerful anti-cancer punch. Pumpkin seeds are an excellent source of zinc, which, as well as being an antioxidant in its own right, aids the absorption of cancer-fighting vitamin A. Among its many health benefits, zinc also helps to strengthen the immune system, promote reproductive health and protect the prostate.

SERVES 4

②③④⑤⑥⑦⑧⑨⑩

1 x 4kg (9lb) pumpkin

4 tsp olive oil

1 large onion, diced

9 slices granary/mixed grain bread, cubed

50g (1¾oz) pumpkin seeds, grilled

50g (1¾oz) sunflower seeds, grilled

150g (5½oz) Gruyère cheese, grated

150g (5½oz) low-fat, low-sodium hard cheese, grated

1 bunch of fresh chervil, chopped

1 litre (1¾ pints) soya milk

15g (½oz) allspice

freshly ground black pepper

1 Create a kind of soup tureen with the pumpkin by slicing off the top to form a lid, which you are going to replace. Scoop out the seeds and the flesh, without piercing the skin. Dice the flesh. Heat the olive oil until very hot and then cook the pumpkin flesh with the onion until tender.

2 Inside the pumpkin shell, make alternate layers of cubed bread, cooked pumpkin flesh, pumpkin and sunflower seeds, the two cheeses and the chervil, finishing with a cheese layer on the top. Reserve a little cheese for a garnish.

3 Whisk the soya milk and allspice together. Season and pour into the pumpkin. Cover with its own lid, wrap carefully in foil and cook in a preheated oven (140°C/275°F/Gas 1) for 2 hours. Serve garnished with chopped chervil.

Fat: 40g (62%) • Protein: 48g (96%) • Carbohydrate: 89g (39%) • Fibre: 13g (54%)
Vitamin A: 240% • Vitamin C: 110% • Calcium: 90% • Iron: 70% • Zinc: 52% • Cholesterol: 16%

VEGETABLES

Broccoli and Almond Risotto

Eating more vegetables will dramatically reduce your risk of disease, but if you really want to swing the odds in favour of a long and healthy life, then you need to eat the right vegetables. You should definitely eat more broccoli: it lowers the risk of cancer – especially of the colon, lung and prostate – and has been shown to block the cell mutations that foreshadow any cancer. For optimum health, eat broccoli three times a week.

SERVES 6   ① ② ④ ⑤ ⑧ ⑨ ⑩

200g (7oz) broccoli

1 red onion, finely diced

1 garlic clove, chopped

90ml (3fl oz) olive oil

300g (10½oz) Arborio rice

1 litre (1¾ pints) vegetable stock

6 fresh sage leaves, sliced

freshly ground black pepper

60ml (2fl oz) almond cream

100g (3½oz) blanched almonds

50g (1¾oz) fresh Parmesan cheese, grated, plus extra shavings to garnish

1 Blanch (cook briefly) the broccoli in a pan of boiling water. In another large pan, cook the diced onion and chopped garlic in the olive oil until tender (do not let them discolour).

2 Add the rice and stir for 2 minutes to coat all the grains. Cover the rice with a little of the hot vegetable stock and cook gently for 10 minutes, stirring frequently.

3 Add the broccoli, sage and seasoning. Gradually add more stock as the rice absorbs all the liquid. Continue to cook until the rice is tender (it should take approximately 25 minutes in total).

4 When the rice is cooked, add the almond cream, whole almonds and Parmesan cheese and stir. Check the seasoning and, just before serving, sprinkle the risotto with Parmesan shavings.

As a variation, use other nuts or different blanched vegetables, for example asparagus or green beans.

FAT: 25G (38%) • PROTEIN: 12G (24%) • CARBOHYDRATE: 49G (16%)
FIBRE: 5G (18%) • VITAMIN E: 48% • CALCIUM: 20% • POTASSIUM: 33%
CHOLESTEROL: 2%

Coriander Potato Bake

Potatoes are high in silica, which is essential for the body's connective tissues, especially lung tissue, which it helps to keep elastic. In healthy people the *Solanaceae* family of vegetables (which includes potatoes) can stop calcium deposits building up. This dish also contains coriander, which has potent antifungal and antibacterial properties (the Romans used it to preserve meats) and is good for both the circulation and the digestive system. Coriander is also an aphrodisiac, so if you're planning a candlelit seduction, serve this dish as your main course.

SERVES 4   ② ③ ④ ⑤ ⑧ ⑩

80g (3oz) tomato purée

200ml (7fl oz) vegetable stock

1kg (2lb 4oz) potatoes, diced

25g (1oz) paprika

8 garlic cloves, chopped

2 tbsp chopped fresh coriander

freshly ground black pepper

60ml (2fl oz) olive oil

1 Mix the tomato purée into the vegetable stock. Put the potatoes, paprika, vegetable stock, garlic and chopped coriander into an ovenproof dish, reserving some of the coriander for garnish. Add the olive oil for flavour.

2 Mix everything together, season, cover and cook in a preheated oven (170°C/325°F/Gas 3) for 1 hour until the potatoes are soft. Check the seasoning and garnish with fresh coriander before serving.

FAT: 13G (20%) • PROTEIN: 9G (18%) • CARBOHYDRATE: 65G (22%)
FIBRE: 8G (32%) • VITAMIN A: 120% • VITAMIN C: 120% • VITAMIN E: 16%
CHOLESTEROL: 0

Imam Bayildi (Turkish Stuffed Aubergines)

This cholesterol-free Turkish dish is packed with potassium, which unites with phosphorous to send oxygen to the brain. Potassium keeps blood pressure stable and skin healthy and is critical to the synthesis of protein and nucleic acids. Aubergines help maintain lower blood cholesterol, prevent plaque building up in the arteries and have both antibacterial and diuretic properties.

SERVES 6   ③ ④ ⑥ ⑦ ⑨ ⑩

200g (7oz) raisins

6 aubergines

juice of 2 lemons

100ml (3½fl oz) olive oil

5 large onions, finely chopped

5 tbsp chopped fresh flat-leaved parsley

10 tomatoes, skinned, deseeded and chopped

5 garlic cloves, crushed

1 pinch of cayenne pepper

1 sprig of fresh thyme

3 bay leaves

freshly ground black pepper

1 Soak the raisins in a bowl of warm water. Halve the aubergines lengthways. Extract and dice the flesh without piercing the skins. Mix the flesh with the juice of 1 lemon.
2 Heat the olive oil and sauté the diced aubergines, onions, parsley, tomatoes, crushed garlic, cayenne pepper, thyme and bay leaves. Season and cook for 30 minutes. Drain the raisins and add to this mixture when cooked.
3 Place the empty aubergine skins in an ovenproof dish. Stuff them with the vegetable mixture and cook in a preheated oven (160°C/325°F/Gas 3) for 1½ hours. Squeeze over the juice of the second lemon before serving.

To make this a meat dish, add 300g (10½oz) of lean minced lamb to the stuffing with the raisins.

Avoid aubergines if you suffer from arthritis.

FAT: 17G (27%) • PROTEIN: 10G (20%) • CARBOHYDRATE: 78G (26%)
FIBRE: 19G (77%) • VITAMIN C: 120% • POTASSIUM: 229% • CHOLESTEROL: 0

Summer Tabbouleh

A diet that is high in antioxidant-rich tomatoes is linked with low rates of both pancreatic and cervical cancer. Tomatoes are the best source of lycopene – a lesser known carotenoid that researchers now believe is a more potent antioxidant than betacarotene. Blood levels of lycopene drop with age and if you are over 50 and do not suffer from arthritis, you should try to eat a tomato or tomato product a day.

SERVES 6   ② ③ ④ ⑥ ⑦ ⑧

1 cucumber

500g (1lb 2oz) bulgar wheat

juice of 3 lemons

100ml (3½fl oz) olive oil

4 ripe beef tomatoes, skinned, deseeded and chopped

6 tbsp chopped fresh parsley

4 tbsp chopped fresh coriander

3 tbsp chopped fresh mint

1 large onion, thinly sliced

freshly ground black pepper

1 Peel the cucumber and slice it in half. Scrape out the seeds with a teaspoon and cut the flesh into small cubes.
2 Cook the bulgar wheat in boiling water for 15 minutes until tender. Strain the wheat and leave to rest. When the wheat is cold, add the lemon juice, olive oil, tomatoes, parsley, coriander, mint, sliced onion, cucumber and seasoning. Chill for at least 2 hours before serving.

For a change, you can make this dish with couscous. For the best results, make the tabbouleh 24 hours before you want to serve it.

FAT: 17G (26%) • PROTEIN: 13G (26%) • CARBOHYDRATE: 68G (23%)
FIBRE: 11G (45%) • VITAMIN C: 35% • MAGNESIUM: 45%
POTASSIUM: 69% • CHOLESTEROL: 0

Spinach and Goats' Cheese Lasagne

It gave Popeye his muscles, but spinach is actually more likely to lower levels of homocysteine, a blood protein that is now recognized as a major indicator of heart disease. Spinach also prevents premature ageing, protects eyesight, boosts immunity and gives you strong bones and teeth. Spinach contains vitamin A which, as well as fighting cancer, supports the body's natural defences and helps to regulate hormones. The nuts in this recipe contain vitamin E, which is said to slow down the ageing process.

SERVES 4   ① ③ ④ ⑤ ⑧ ⑩

500g (1lb 2oz) fresh spinach

¼ tsp freshly grated nutmeg

50g (1¾oz) mixed nuts, including pecans, walnuts, hazelnuts, brazil nuts, all finely chopped

½ tsp ground coriander

40g (1½oz) soya spread

40g (1½oz) plain flour (use wheat-free if you have allergies)

600ml (1 pint) soya milk

200g (7oz) organic soft goats' cheese

½ tsp English mustard

freshly ground black pepper

175g (6oz) wholewheat lasagne (use corn pasta if avoiding wheat)

paprika, to garnish

1 Cook the spinach in a large saucepan with a little water until it goes limp. Grate in the nutmeg and stir in the chopped nuts and the ground coriander.

2 In a small pan, make a bechamel sauce: gently melt the soya spread, add the flour and cook for 2 minutes, stirring all the time. Add the soya milk gradually and bring to the boil, again stirring constantly. Simmer gently for a few more minutes until the sauce thickens.

3 Melt the goats' cheese into the sauce, keeping some back to sprinkle on the top of the finished dish. Stir in the mustard and season to taste.

4 Layer the spinach and nut mixture with the sheets of lasagne in an ovenproof dish. Pour the goats' cheese sauce over the top and sprinkle the last layer with the reserved cheese and paprika.

5 Bake at the top of a preheated oven (190°C/375°F/Gas mark 5) for 30 minutes and serve, piping hot, with crusty bread and a green salad.

FAT: 29G (44%) • PROTEIN: 23G (46%) • CARBOHYDRATE: 30G (10%)
FIBRE: 8G (32%) • VITAMIN A: 190% • VITAMIN E: 39% • FOLATE: 69%
CHOLESTEROL: 8%

Parsnip and Horseradish Mash

Parsnips are frequently underrated. As well as tasting delicious, they have important health benefits. They contain more soluble fibre than any other everyday vegetable, helping to lower cholesterol, reduce blood pressure, and sweep cancer-causing agents through the colon and out of the body. Parsnips also contain six different types of anti-cancer agents. The horseradish in this tasty dish is a decongestant that loosens mucus, helping to clear respiratory disorders, including asthma and bronchitis. It also speeds up the metabolism slightly to burn more calories.

SERVES 4   ② ④ ⑧

200g (7oz) potatoes, cut into chunks

800g (1lb 12oz) parsnips, cut into chunks

200ml (7fl oz) soya cream

150ml (5fl oz) olive oil

3 tsp fresh horseradish, grated

1 pinch of freshly grated nutmeg

freshly ground black pepper

1 Cook the potatoes and parsnips together until soft. Heat up the soya cream.

2 Drain the vegetables and mash with the hot soya cream, slowly drizzling the olive oil into the pan as you mash. Add the remaining ingredients, season and serve.

As an alternative, make the same dish with swedes or turnips instead of parsnips.

FAT: 40G (62%) • PROTEIN: 4G (8%) • CARBOHYDRATE: 54G (18%)
FIBRE: 9G (35%) • VITAMIN C: 70% • POTASSIUM: 125% • CHOLESTEROL: 0

Cauliflower and Roquefort Fricassée

Walnuts are a concentrated source of omega-3 essential acids, which can lower high cholesterol and high blood pressure, reduce elevated blood tryglyceride levels and help prevent blood clots. Even better, they can lower high levels of the protein homocysteine, which are now reckoned to be an even better indicator of a risk of heart problems than cholesterol. Walnuts are a good alternative to oily fish (also rich in omega-3 fatty acids) if you are vegetarian or are worried about eating fish that contains environmental toxins.

SERVES 4 ① ④ ⑤ ⑥ ⑧ ⑨

1 large head of cauliflower, cut into florets

300g (10½oz) celery stalks, sliced

½ lemon

40ml (1½fl oz) olive oil

4 tbsp chopped fresh parsley

100g (3½oz) black grapes, halved

50g (1¾oz) walnuts

freshly ground black pepper

150ml (5fl oz) vegetable stock

125g (4oz) Roquefort cheese, diced

1 Blanch (cook briefly) the cauliflower florets, together with the celery and the lemon, in boiling water. (The lemon keeps the cauliflower white.) Drain well, discard the lemon and sauté the cauliflower and celery in olive oil until they start to brown.

2 Add the parsley, grape halves and walnuts. Season and cook for 5–7 minutes. Transfer this mix to a gratin dish. Heat the stock to boiling. Add to the dish and sprinkle the diced Roquefort over the top.

3 Bake in a preheated oven (180°C/350°F/Gas mark 4) for 20 minutes. Serve piping hot with a young spinach leaf salad on the side.

For variety, try this dish with Stilton or your own favourite blue cheese.

FAT: 26G (41%) • PROTEIN: 14G (28%) • CARBOHYDRATE: 22G (7%)
FIBRE: 7G (28%) • VITAMIN C: 250% • CALCIUM: 30%
OMEGA-3 FATTY ACIDS: 37% • CHOLESTEROL: 9%

Black-eyed Bean Balti

This potassium-rich curry will boost energy levels and help maintain a healthy heart and circulation. Ginger is native to India, where traditional Ayurvedic medicine uses it as a spiritual cleanser, and as a digestive aid. Ginger has many health benefits: it is an excellent antidepressant, and it boosts the immune system, warding off colds and flu. Ginger also quells both travel and morning sickness and is used in some cultures to help treat impotence.

SERVES 4 ① ② ④ ⑥ ⑦ ⑨ ⑩

300g (10½oz) black-eyed beans

4 bay leaves

3 cardamom pods

3 garlic cloves, crushed

½ tsp ground turmeric

40g (1½oz) fresh root ginger, grated

2 dried red chillies, crushed and deseeded

40ml (1½fl oz) olive oil

1 tsp ground cumin

100g (3½oz) low-fat natural yogurt

3 sprigs of fresh coriander, chopped, to garnish

3 onions, finely chopped

4 tomatoes

1 Soak the beans for 12 hours in cold water. Cook them slowly for 1 hour in boiling water with the bay leaves, cardamom, half the crushed garlic and the turmeric until tender. When cooked, drain and reserve the liquid.

2 In a balti dish or a large, heavy-based saucepan, cook the onions, tomatoes, ginger, remaining garlic and chillies in olive oil for 5 minutes. Add the ground cumin, black-eyed beans, yogurt and some of the reserved liquid.

3 Cook for another 5 minutes until the sauce thickens. Garnish with fresh, chopped coriander and serve with rice or chapatis.

FAT: 11G (17%) • PROTEIN: 11G (22%) • CARBOHYDRATE: 38G (13%)
FIBRE: 10G (40%) • VITAMIN C: 60% • FOLATE: 37% • POTASSIUM: 93%
CHOLESTEROL: 0

Country Bean and Lentil Pie

Never underestimate the humble bean, which provides colon-cleansing fibre, energy-boosting iron and heart-protecting folate. In this dish, the often over-looked red kidney bean reigns supreme and provides the calcium and iron that is lacking in so many over-refined diets. The lentil had a hippy image, but is now served in all the most fashionable restaurants in the world's capital cities. It is also an important ingredient in trendy fusion cuisine.

SERVES 6   ① ② ③ ❹ ❻ ❽ ⑩

3 small white onions, diced

2 garlic cloves, crushed

50ml (2fl oz) olive oil

1 medium-sized aubergine, cut into chunks

2 medium-sized carrots, cut into chunks

2 courgettes, cut into chunks

900ml (1½ pints) vegetable stock

2 large beef tomatoes, skinned, deseeded and chopped

400g (14oz) chickpeas, soaked and cooked

150g (5½oz) red lentils

400g (14oz) red kidney beans, soaked and cooked

400g (14oz) green flageolet beans soaked and cooked with sage leaves

1 tbsp sunflower seeds

2 tsp tomato purée

splash of Tabasco and soy sauce, to taste

freshly ground black pepper

half a dozen fresh sage leaves, roughly chopped

For the topping:

400g (14oz) potatoes, suitable for mashing, chopped

3 tbsp low-fat crème fraîche

100g (3½oz) Feta cheese

1 In a heavy-based saucepan, gently soften the onion and garlic in the olive oil. Add the chunky chopped vegetables (aubergine, carrots, courgettes) and cook gently until tender but still firm.

2 Pour in the vegetable stock and add the beef tomatoes. Add the chickpeas, red lentils, red kidney beans, green flageolet beans and sunflower seeds. Stir in the tomato purée and add a splash each of Tabasco and soy sauce to taste.

3 Cook on the hob for 15 minutes over a medium heat until all the vegetables are cooked but still firm. Pour this mixture into the base of an ovenproof casserole dish. Season to taste and add the roughly chopped sage leaves.

4 To make the topping, boil the potatoes until soft. Mash them with low-fat crème fraîche and roughly crumble the Feta cheese into the mixture, reserving some for the top. Spread this mash over the vegetable mix and crumble the reserved Feta cheese on top.

5 Heat through in a preheated oven (170°C/325°F/Gas 3) until the top has browned. Serve like a country cottage pie with French beans or cabbage.

This dish is also delicious cold, sliced into lunchbox-size portions.

FAT: 6G (9%) • PROTEIN: 38G (76%) • CARBOHYDRATE: 109G (36%) • FIBRE: 37G (147%)
VITAMIN A: 120% • FOLATE: 105% • IRON: 70% • CHOLESTEROL: 0

Riot of Chunky Vegetables

As well as a blast of the most potent antioxidant nutrients, this meal provides almost 50 per cent of the minimum daily intake of vitamin D. Crucial for bone growth, vitamin D helps the body use both calcium and phosphorous. We cannot utilize the vitamin D we get from either our diet or supplements directly, but must convert it first to an active form. This job is carried out by the liver, which is why people with liver and kidney disease are at a higher risk of osteoporosis (brittle bone disease) than others.

SERVES 6　①②③❹⑤❻❼❽❾

1 head of cauliflower, cut into florets	**800ml (1½ pints) soya milk**
6 large carrots, cut into chunks	**1 egg yolk**
250g (9oz) swede, cut into chunks	**125g (4oz) Emmental cheese, grated**
500g (1lb 2oz) potatoes, cut into chunks	**3 tbsp chopped fresh flat-leaved parsley**
3 fresh sage leaves	**1 pinch of freshly grated nutmeg**
60g (2oz) soya spread	**freshly ground black pepper**
60g (2oz) white flour	**6 hardboiled eggs, shelled**

1 Cook the cauliflower, carrots, swede and potatoes with the sage leaves in boiling water until tender but still firm. Drain and rinse.

2 Melt the soya spread in a heavy-based saucepan. Add the flour and whisk well. Cook for 2–3 minutes, then start adding the cold milk, a little at a time, stirring constantly.

3 Bring to a gentle boil and cook for another 2 minutes. Add the egg yolk, Emmental (reserving a little to top the dish), chopped parsley and grated nutmeg. Season.

4 Put all the cooked vegetables in an ovenproof dish. Cut the hard-boiled eggs in half and arrange in the same dish. Pour over the cheesy white sauce and sprinkle the reserved cheese over the top. Bake in a preheated oven (180°C/350°F/Gas 4) for 20–25 minutes until the top is golden brown. Serve with garlic and rosemary bread *(see page 38)* and a mixed green side salad.

If you like, try adding 100g (3½oz) of tuna to the white sauce before baking.

FAT: 20G (31%) • PROTEIN: 23G (46%) • CARBOHYDRATE: 47G (16%)
FIBRE: 7G (28%) • VITAMIN A: 440% • VITAMIN C: 160% • VITAMIN D: 47%
POTASSIUM: 160% • CHOLESTEROL: 89%

Spicy French Beans with Pine Nuts

In general, the darker and more intensely coloured the vegetable, the higher its levels of nutrients. This high-fibre, zero-cholesterol side-dish contains bright-green parsley, which is an excellent source of vitamins. In fact, parsley is so potent that you only need to eat very small amounts. Parsley helps support adrenal and thyroid functions, aids digestion, and contains a chemical said to prevent the multiplication of tumour cells. It is also used traditionally as a breath freshener.

SERVES 4　②❹❻❽❾⑩

800g (1lb 12oz) French beans	**60g (2oz) pine kernels, roasted**
60ml (2fl oz) olive oil	**2 garlic cloves, crushed**
2 shallots, diced	**75g (3oz) fresh flat-leaved parsley, chopped**
1 red chilli, deseeded and chopped	**freshly ground black pepper**

1 Cook the French beans until *al dente* (cooked but slightly crunchy) in plenty of boiling water. To stop the cooking and fix the luxuriant green chlorophyll colour, drop them in a pan of cold water as soon as they are cooked.

2 Heat the olive oil in a wok and sauté the diced shallots, chilli, pine kernels and garlic for 5 minutes. Add the French beans and parsley. Season, sauté for a few more minutes and serve immediately.

FAT: 22G (33%) • PROTEIN: 8G (16%) • CARBOHYDRATE: 23G (8%)
FIBRE: 9G (37%) • VITAMIN C: 100% • POTASSIUM: 70% • CHOLESTEROL: 0

Glazed Yams

Potent anti-cancer agents, yams are so effective that one study by The National Cancer Institute in the United States found that men who ate half a cup of yams every day were half as likely to develop lung cancer as those who ate almost none. Yams are included in the list of sources of phytochemicals that a growing number of researchers now believe can not only prevent many degenerative diseases but actually reverse them.

SERVES 4   ③ ❹ ❻ ❽ ❾

800g (1lb 12oz) yams	2.5cm (1in) fresh root ginger, grated
75g (2½oz) brown sugar	
50g (1¾oz) honey	1 pinch of freshly grated nutmeg
5 tsp orange juice	freshly ground black pepper

1 Boil the yams in plenty of water until just tender. Drain and cut into 2.5cm (1in) long slices. Arrange these in a flat, ovenproof dish.
2 Combine the sugar, honey, orange juice, grated ginger and nutmeg in a bowl. Pour this mixture over the yams. Season and cook in a preheated oven (200°C/400°F/Gas 6) until golden.

As an alternative to yams, use parsnip or swede in this dish.

Fat: 0.5g (1%) • Protein: 3g (6%) • Carbohydrate: 77g (26%)
Fibre: 4g (15%) • Vitamin A: 680% • Vitamin C: 60% • Cholesterol: 0

Ladies' Fingers (Okra) with Lime

Okra can help protect the intestinal tract. It can relieve irritation of the lining of the gut and is effective against disorders such as stomach ulcers and colitis. The folate in this dish can help improve skin condition and its cholesterol-lowering, antioxidant vitamin C will help fight cancer.

SERVES 6   ❶ ❷ ❹ ❾

1kg (2lb 4oz) ladies' fingers (Okra)	3 tsp ground cumin
3 spring onions, sliced	freshly ground black pepper
3 garlic cloves, crushed	juice of 2 limes
60ml (2fl oz) olive oil	2 sprigs of fresh flat-leaved parsley
1 red pepper, diced	

1 Trim the okra and slice into 1cm (½in) pieces.
2 Cook the spring onions and garlic in olive oil for 5 minutes. Add the okra, red pepper and cumin. Season and cook for 15 minutes until the okra is soft. Just before serving, add the lime juice and chopped parsley.

To make this into a main course dish, add prawns.

Fat: 10g (15%) • Protein: 5g (8%) • Carbohydrate: 15g (5%)
Fibre: 5g (19%) • Vitamin C: 90% • Folate: 20% • Cholesterol: 0

Tian of Summer Vegetables

This is a traditional dish from the South of France where rates of heart disease are low, despite a high-fat diet washed down with lots of red wine. The aubergines prevent the rise of blood cholesterol, protect the arteries from plaque deposits and enhance the immune system. The high potassium content, which regulates heartbeat, will also help to keep your muscles and your nervous system healthy.

SERVES 6

2 garlic cloves, crushed

3 onions, chopped

175ml (6fl oz) olive oil

1 tsp coriander seeds

6 courgettes, cut into ½cm (¼ in) slices

4 long, narrow aubergines, cut into ½cm (¼ in) slices

750g (1lb 11oz) tomatoes, cut into ½cm (¼ in) slices

6 bay leaves

1 sprig of fresh thyme

1 sprig of fresh oregano

3 star anises, crushed

1 Sauté the crushed garlic and chopped onion in 8 tsp (40ml) of the olive oil for 5 minutes, until slightly golden. Mix in the coriander seeds. In a large, flat, oven-proof dish, spread out the onion and coriander seed mix so that it covers the entire tray.

2 On top of this, arrange the sliced vegetables neatly in alternate rows starting with the courgettes in one line, the aubergines in the next, followed by the tomatoes. Continue this sequence until the entire tray has been covered with the sliced vegetables.

3 Slide the bay leaves between these rows. Strip the oregano and thyme leaves from their stems and sprinkle the leaves on top of the rows of vegetables, together with the crushed star anises.

4 Pour the remaining olive oil evenly over the top of all the herbs and vegetables. Cook slowly in a preheated oven (110°C/225°F/Gas ¼) for 1½ hours. You can serve this dish hot or cold.

Avoid aubergines if you suffer from arthritis.

FAT: 29G (44%) • PROTEIN: 5G (10%) • CARBOHYDRATE: 37G (12%)
FIBRE: 12G (49%) • VITAMIN C: 70% • POTASSIUM: 152% • CHOLESTEROL: 0

Roasted Celeriac with Sage

Lack of vitamin B2 (riboflavin) is one of the most common nutritional deficiencies among adults in the United States. To improve your levels of riboflavin, try this recipe, full of vitamin B-rich celeriac. Unlike its close relative vitamin B1 (thiamine), riboflavin is not destroyed by heat. Also known as vitamin G, riboflavin boosts the immune system, helps regulate hormones, improves skin condition and helps relieve stress. Oats, another ingredient, also keep you calm, making this a superb stress-busting dish. In addition, oats are one of the most effective cholesterol-lowering foods and are an excellent aid for the digestion.

SERVES 6

1kg (2lb 4oz) celeriac, peeled

1 sprig of fresh thyme

5 garlic cloves, left in the skin

100ml (3½fl oz) olive oil

freshly ground black pepper

150g (5½oz) rolled oats

15 fresh sage leaves, chopped

1 Dice the celeriac into 3cm (1¼in) square cubes and blanch them in boiling water. Drain and dry them with kitchen paper. Lay out the celeriac cubes with the thyme and garlic cloves in a deep roasting tray.

2 Pour over the olive oil, season and cook in a preheated oven (200°C/400°F/Gas 6) for 20 minutes.

3 Sprinkle the oats into the dish and cook for another 10 minutes until the celeriac is golden coloured and crispy. Just before serving, top with the chopped sage leaves.

FAT: 19G (29%) • PROTEIN: 6G (12%) • CARBOHYDRATE: 30G (10%)
FIBRE: 5G (20%) • VITAMIN B2: 10% • VITAMIN C: 20% • CHOLESTEROL: 0

Swiss Chard – Two Ways

This power-packed, anti-cancer dish could not be simpler or healthier. Chard corrects calcium deficiency, regulates digestive function and acts as a diuretic. The chlorophyll-rich leaves will also help keep your breath fresh.

SERVES 6 ② ④ ⑤ ⑥ ⑦ ⑧ ⑨

For the first way:

1.5kg (3lb 6oz) Swiss chard

100g (3½oz) fresh Parmesan cheese, grated

50g (1¾oz) breadcrumbs

freshly ground black pepper

60ml (2fl oz) vegetable stock

For the second way:

1.5kg (3lb 6oz) Swiss chard

2 garlic cloves, crushed

1 sprig each of fresh rosemary and thyme

60ml (2fl oz) olive oil

freshly ground black pepper

50g (1¾oz) fresh flat-leaved parsley, chopped

For the first way:

1 Wash and dry the Swiss chard and separate the green leaves from the white ribs, reserving both. Blanch the leaves in boiling water, drain and dry. Mix the Parmesan with the breadcrumbs and season.

2 In a flat-bottomed, ovenproof dish, start to build layers of chard leaves and cheese, like a lasagne. Start with the chard and end with the Parmesan. To keep the dish moist, pour the vegetable stock over each of these layers.

3 Bake for 25 minutes in an oven preheated to 180°C/350°F/Gas 4 until the cheese has browned.

For the second way:

1 Separate the chard leaves from the ribs as before. Cut the ribs into small strips and, in a casserole dish on the hob, cook them and the green leaves with the crushed garlic, rosemary and thyme in olive oil until tender but still firm.

2 Season, cover and cook for 20 minutes over a medium heat. Add the parsley and stir well before serving.

> FAT: 16G (24%) • PROTEIN: 13G (26%) • CARBOHYDRATE: 17G (6%)
> FIBRE: 5G (19%) • VITAMIN A: 180% • VITAMIN C: 140% • CALCIUM: 17MG (47%)
> POTASSIUM: 118% • CHOLESTEROL: 4%

Braised Fennel

A natural appetite suppressant, fennel is a useful food for weight-loss management. It can also relieve the symptoms of irritable bowel syndrome (IBS) and works to support the liver, kidneys and spleen. High in the antioxidant vitamins A and C, it has anti-cancer properties, strengthens the immune system and can help to keep the lungs clear.

SERVES 6 ① ② ④ ⑥ ⑧ ⑨

4 large fennel bulbs

½ lemon (not consumed)

1 onion, sliced

125g (4oz) carrots, sliced

700ml (1¼ pints) vegetable (or chicken) stock

2 bay leaves

1 sprig of fresh thyme

freshly ground black pepper

50g (1¾ oz) fresh parsley, chopped, to garnish

1 Trim, wash and remove both the stalks and the leaves from the fennel bulbs. Cook in boiling water with the lemon half for 15 minutes. Discard the lemon. Drain well and cut the fennel in half, lengthways.

2 Put the sliced onion and carrots in the bottom of a casserole dish. Add the fennel, cover with the stock and add the bay leaves and thyme. Season.

3 Cover with a tight-fitting lid. If you don't have one, cover the dish with greaseproof paper. Cook in a preheated oven (140°C/275°F/Gas 1) for 1½ hours. Serve garnished with chopped fresh parsley.

You can braise any type of vegetable in this way.

> FAT: 1G (1%) • PROTEIN: 3G (6%) • CARBOHYDRATE: 18G (6%)
> FIBRE: 6G (25%) • VITAMIN A: 110% • VITAMIN C: 60% • CHOLESTEROL: 0

Banana and Rosemary Tatin

Everyone knows bananas are rich in energy-giving potassium, which protects the heart, but it's less well known that they feed the 'good' bacteria in the digestive tract, improving the digestion. Bananas encourage the production of serotonin, a mood-enhancing hormone and, because they are low in fat, they are a useful weight-control aid. Rosemary stimulates the circulation, maintains healthy blood pressure and is an antibacterial agent. It can relieve migraine headaches and, in folklore, it is said to improve concentration and memory.

SERVES 6   ❷ ❹ ❻ ❼ ❾

12 bananas	**1 sprig of fresh rosemary**
juice of 1 lemon	**20g (¾oz) roasted almond flakes**
20g (¾oz) soya spread	**300g (10½oz) puff pastry**
125g (4oz) caster sugar	**125ml (4fl oz) water**

1 Cut the bananas into 6cm (2½in) batons and mix them with the lemon juice. Line the bottom of a round, shallow tart tin (18cm/7in diameter, fixed bottom) with greaseproof paper.

2 Melt the soya spread and sugar in a saucepan. Bring to a gentle boil, cook until the liquid turns a golden caramel colour, then pour it into the tart tin.

3 Place a few leaves of fresh rosemary in the sauce and arrange the banana batons, standing upright, in a very tight circle to cover the entire bottom of the tin. Insert the roasted almond flakes between the banana batons.

4 Roll the puff pastry out to form a circle that is 3mm (⅛in) thick and at least 3cm (1¼in) wider in circumference than the tart tin. Cover the bananas and fold the excess pastry down in between the edge of the tin and the outside ring of banana. (The puff pastry will eventually become the base of the tatin when it is turned upside down.)

5 Make a hole in the middle of the secured pastry to release steam and pour in the water to create a sauce and stop the caramel from burning while the fruit cooks. Place in a preheated oven (190°C/375°F/Gas 5) for 20–25 minutes until the puff pastry is cooked. When you take the tin out of the oven, place a large plate or tray over the top and, carefully but quickly, turn the tin and the tray upside down.

6 Leave the tatin to rest for 15 minutes, then gently remove the tin. Do not force it. If it sticks, use a sharp-edged knife to free the pastry edges from the dish. Serve warm on its own or with vanilla ice cream. *(See page 116 for a dairy-free ice cream recipe.)*

Tatin means 'reversed' so you make this dish, cook it and turn it upside down to present it.

FAT: 24G (37%) • PROTEIN: 7G (14%) • CARBOHYDRATE: 104G (35%) • FIBRE: 7G (27%)
VITAMIN C: 40% • POTASSIUM: 110% • CHOLESTEROL: 10%

Strawberry Soup with Red Wine

A powerful antioxidant, strawberries can protect against DNA damage and gram for gram contain more fibre than wholegrain bread. High in potassium, strawberries also act as antiviral agents and are effective against the herpes virus, which causes cold sores. Red wine is believed to contain a non-alcoholic chemical that may prevent the formation of the plaque that blocks the arteries increasing the risk of stroke and heart disease. The fresh mint in this dish will lessen the length of time food spends in the stomach by stimulating gastric juices and can also help relieve insomnia and migraine headaches.

SERVES 6　　　　　　　　　　② ③ ④ ⑧

250g (9oz) caster sugar

900ml (1½ pints) red wine

2 standard tea bags

10 green peppercorns

1.2 kg (2lb 11oz) fresh strawberries

20 fresh mint leaves, chopped

1 Bring the sugar, wine, tea bags and green peppercorns to the boil in a saucepan and cook until the liquid thickens. Strain and return to the pan.
2 Wash the strawberries and drain them well. Take the tails off and cut each one in two. Add them to the liquid in the saucepan and cook for 3 minutes. Serve in small bowls, sprinkled with chopped mint leaves.

In France, this dish is served either warm or ice cold.

FAT: 1G (1%) (SATURATED FAT: 0) • PROTEIN: 2G (4%) • CARBOHYDRATE: 59G (20%)
FIBRE: 5G (18%) • VITAMIN C: 200% • POTASSIUM: 56% • CHOLESTEROL: 0

Pain d'Epices

The Japanese serve ginger slices between sushi courses to cleanse the palate and aid digestion. In the West, ginger has long been used to settle the stomach, but it can also relieve stiff muscles and aching joints. The star anise in this rustic and old-fashioned dish also promotes healthy digestion and increases mental clarity. You'll be hard pressed to find another dessert that is as low in fat – it has less than a gram of saturated fats – and as rich in dietary fibre as this delicious bread-type pudding.

SERVES 8　　　　　　　　　　② ③ ④ ⑥

100ml (3½fl oz) organic milk (use soya if intolerant to lactose)

1 tsp ground ginger

1 cinnamon stick

8 cloves

10g (½oz) star anise

100g (3½oz) sugar

350ml (12fl oz) maple syrup, plus 120ml (4fl oz) to glaze

250g (9oz) white flour (use gluten-free if intolerant)

250g (9oz) rye flour

10g (½oz) baking powder (gluten-free if intolerant)

3 eggs, beaten

1 Bring the milk to the boil, add the spices and leave to infuse for 30 minutes. Strain the milk, add the sugar and maple syrup and re-warm it.
2 In a bowl, combine the two flours and the baking powder. Slowly add the warm milk and the eggs and mix well. Line a 500g (1lb) loaf tin with greaseproof paper and pour in the loaf mix.
3 Bake in a preheated oven (180°C/350°F/Gas 4) for 1 hour. To check if the loaf is cooked, pierce the centre with a thin metal skewer and pull back out. If it comes out dry, the pudding is done. Remove from the tin and brush the whole loaf with maple syrup.

This dish always tastes better 24 hours after cooking, when all the flavours have fully infused the loaf. Slice and serve with Quick Confiture *(see page 114)* or pack for a picnic lunch.

FAT: 3.5G (6%) • PROTEIN: 9G (18%) • CARBOHYDRATE: 106G (35%)
FIBRE: 6G (25%) • VITAMIN B3: 23% • IRON: 20% • POTASSIUM: 55%
CHOLESTEROL: 27%

Summer Honey and Lavender Crème Brulée

Even the name of this dish conjures up an uplifting picture of the perfect English summer with the bees buzzing around the lavender flowers. The bees' honey and the plants' flowers combine in this Catalan-inspired dish. The healing power of honey, nature's sweetener, is well documented. It can help treat an enormous number of disorders, from acne to rheumatism. Lavender has an antidepressant, calming effect and helps lower blood pressure. Eat this pudding as a special treat when you need cheering up.

SERVES 6 ❸ ❹ ❻ ❼

4 egg yolks	600ml (1 pint) soya cream
25g (1oz) cornflour	25g (1oz) honey
150g (5½oz) caster sugar	6 lavender flower heads

1 Whisk the egg yolks, cornflour and 100g (3½oz) of the sugar together until the mixture is white and foamy.
2 In a saucepan, gently heat the soya cream, honey and lavender flowers until just below boiling point. (You will see the surface just begin to bubble.) Pass the hot liquid through a fine sieve into the bowl containing the foamy egg and sugar mixture, whisking constantly.
3 Return the mixture to the saucepan and cook very slowly until the custard thickens. Remove from the heat and keep stirring until it has cooled and is just warm.
4 Pour the custard into six small ramekin dishes and chill until cold. Before serving, cover the top of each dish with the reserved sugar. Pop under a hot grill to caramelize the top. It should be crispy and golden brown, almost burnt.

Fat: 34g (52%) • Protein: 6g (12%) • Carbohydrate: 96g (32%)
Vitamin D: 8% • Phosphorous: 47% • Potassium: 84% • Cholesterol: 48%

Honey and Fig Loaf

High in fibre, figs fight cancer, can ward off bacterial infections and may be eaten as a natural laxative. They can also help prevent painful haemorrhoids and are often fed to convalescing patients because they can speed up recovery from illness. Pure honey contains 180 different nutrients and curative substances; it is also the best form of carbohydrate for human consumption because it is the most easily digested.

SERVES 6 ❷ ❹ ❻ ❽

175g (6oz) wholemeal flour (use gluten-free if intolerant)	150ml (5fl oz) organic milk (use soya milk if lactose-intolerant)
½ tsp salt	½ tsp bicarbonate of soda
2 tbsp honey	100g (3½oz) dried figs

1 Mix the flour and salt in a large bowl and form a well in the centre. Melt the honey in half the milk on the hob and dissolve the bicarbonate of soda in the reserved cold milk.
2 Take the warmed milk and honey off the stove and combine it with the cold milk and bicarbonate of soda. Pour the milk into the well in the middle of the flour. Add the dried figs and mix well.
3 Transfer this mixture to a 500g (1lb) loaf tin, which you have lined with greaseproof paper. Cook in a preheated oven (170°C/325°F/Gas 3) for about 40 minutes until you can pierce the loaf with a skewer and it comes out clean. Leave the loaf to rest a few hours before eating.

You can replace the figs with dried apricots or sultanas.

Fat: 1g (1%) • Protein: 5g (10%) • Carbohydrate: 39g (13%)
Fibre: 6g (22%) • Iron: 8% • Potassium: 31% • Cholesterol: 0

Quick Confiture – Guava or Pineapple

Change the fruit and see how the nutritional breakdown of the entire dish changes. Guava is high in fibre and crammed with stress-busting, cancer-fighting vitamin C. Pineapple has relatively little vitamin C but the lemon juice compensates for this. Pineapple contains an enzyme called bromelain, which has powerful anti-inflammatory and digestive properties. It enhances the absorption of other nutrients and is now believed to be beneficial to the cardiovascular system, too.

SERVES 4   ② ④ ⑥ ⑧ ⑨ ⑩

For Guava Confiture:

500g (1lb 2oz) guava

250g (9oz) sugar

400ml (14fl oz) water

¼ vanilla pod

juice of 1 lemon

1 Wash and remove the head of the guava. Peel and cut the fruit into slices and discard the excess seeds.
2 In a heavy-based saucepan, dissolve the sugar in the water; add the fruit, vanilla and lemon juice. Cook slowly for 1 hour, until the fruit is very soft. Serve warm or cold the same day.

For Pineapple Confiture:

500g (1lb 2oz) fresh pineapple

200g (7oz) sugar

200ml (7fl oz) water

¼ vanilla pod

juice of 1 lemon

1 Peel the pineapple and dice into small cubes.
2 Dissolve the sugar in the water, add the pineapple, vanilla pod and lemon juice. Cook for 30–45 minutes, until the fruit is soft.

> GUAVA: FAT: 1G (2%) • PROTEIN: 1G (2%) • CARBOHYDRATE: 78G (26%) FIBRE: 7G (27%) • VITAMIN A: 20% • VITAMIN C: 390% • CHOLESTEROL: 0
> PINEAPPLE: FAT: 0.5G (1%) • PROTEIN: 1G (2%) • CARBOHYDRATE: 79G (26%) FIBRE: 2G (6%) • VITAMIN C: 35% • MANGANESE: 8% • CHOLESTEROL: 0

Carrot and Walnut Cake

Energizing carrots, which detoxify and cleanse the body, contain large amounts of betacarotenes, which are potent anti-cancer agents. Carrots can slow the growth of 'bad' bacteria in the digestive tract and will improve the quality of hair, skin and nails. They can counter stress, protect against macular degeneration (eye disease) and, if eaten every day, help regulate the menstrual cycle. Walnuts are high in vitamin A, potassium, magnesium and omega-3 fatty acids.

SERVES 6   ② ③ ④ ⑥ ⑧ ⑨ ⑩

200g (7oz) sugar

1 tbsp walnut oil

5 tsp vanilla essence

4 eggs, beaten

250g (9oz) wholemeal flour (use gluten-free, if intolerant)

2 tsp baking powder

100g (3½oz) carrots, grated

50g (1¾oz) sultanas

80g (3oz) walnuts, chopped

1 Mix together the sugar, oil and vanilla essence. Add the eggs, one by one, stirring vigorously. Add the flour, baking powder, grated carrots, sultanas and walnuts.
2 Transfer this mixture to a 500g (1lb) loaf tin lined with greaseproof paper. Cook for 1 hour in a preheated oven (160°C/325°F/Gas 3). Pierce the centre with a metal skewer. If it comes out clean, the cake is done.

Leave this cake to rest for 3–4 hours so that it is stone cold before you cut it.

> FAT: 22G (34%) • PROTEIN: 13G (26%) • CARBOHYDRATE: 44G (15%) FIBRE: 7G (28%) • VITAMIN A: 100% • IRON: 15% • POTASSIUM: 100% CHOLESTEROL: 47%

Pineapple and Papaya Ice Cream

Papaya can be given to help babies on infant formula digest their milk. It soothes digestive disorders and helps break down unwanted toxins, including uric acid, in the body. Soya (or bean curd) contains probably the most powerful of the phytochemicals, which is said to reverse many diseases, including cancer, heart disease and diabetes. Aim to eat at least one serving of soya protein a day, but make sure the product you use has not been genetically modified. This dairy-free ice cream is suitable for the lactose-intolerant.

SERVES 6 ② ⑧ ⑨ ⑩

200g (7oz) fresh pineapple, peeled and cored

100g (3½oz) fresh papaya, peeled and deseeded

200g (7oz) castor sugar

200ml (7fl oz) soya cream

For the vanilla custard:

75g (2¾oz) caster sugar

6 egg yolks

500ml (18fl oz) soya milk

2 vanilla pods, split in half, lengthways

1 To make the custard, whisk the sugar and the egg yolks in a large bowl until pale and foaming. In a saucepan, bring the milk and vanilla pods to boiling point. Take off the heat, strain, and pour the infused milk gently onto the egg mixture, whisking constantly.

2 Transfer this mixture back to the saucepan and cook very gently, over a medium heat, stirring with a metal spoon until the liquid coats the back of the spoon. Take off the heat and transfer to a bowl to cool.

3 Purée the two fruits in a food processor. Transfer to a saucepan with the caster sugar and cook gently for 20 minutes. Leave to cool.

4 When both mixtures are completely cold, combine them with the soya cream and transfer everything to a deep-freezer container. Leave the ice cream mixture to set in the freezer, taking it out and whisking it every 20 minutes or so, until it has hardened. Serve the ice cream with fresh pineapple and papaya slices.

FAT: 10G (16%) • PROTEIN: 6G (12%) • CARBOHYDRATE: 56G (19%)
FIBRE: 2G (7%) • VITAMIN C: 25% • IRON: 8% • POTASSIUM: 32% • CHOLESTEROL: 71%

Passion Fruit Salad

We all know we should eat lots of fresh fruit if we want to be healthy, but lots of people make the mistake of eating fruit straight after a meal. Fruit will only make some digestive disorders worse if you eat it with other food. Instead, eat fruit or this fruit salad for breakfast, as a snack or as a dessert, but wait half an hour after your main course. Most people think of oranges when they crave vitamin C but, in fact, kiwi fruit are a richer source of this important antioxidant and also provide vitamin K, which can help repair thread and varicose veins.

SERVES 6 ① ③ ④ ⑥ ⑦ ⑧ ⑨

250ml (9fl oz) fresh orange juice

250ml (9fl oz) water

200g (7oz) brown sugar

½ pineapple, peeled and diced

3 kiwi fruit, peeled and diced

3 mandarins, broken into segments

2 mangoes, peeled and diced

15 fresh mint leaves, chopped, plus extra to garnish

50g (1¾oz) raspberries

50g (1¾oz) redcurrants

5 passion fruit

2 bananas, optional

1 Bring the orange juice, water and sugar to the boil in a saucepan. Remove from the heat and leave to cool.

2 Mix all the fruits except the raspberries, redcurrants, passion fruit, and bananas (if using) with the chopped mint leaves, and leave to chill for at least 6 hours in the refrigerator. Cover the dish to stop the fruit from drying out in the cold.

3 When ready to serve, mix the chilled fruits, the raspberries and the redcurrants with the cold syrup. Cut the passion fruit in half, scoop out the pulp and mix with the fruit salad. Serve this dish very cold, garnished with chopped mint leaves.

For variety, experiment with the fruits you use. Be as adventurous as you like, but to prevent them discolouring, always mix in the bananas at the end (if using), along with the red fruits (which otherwise will colour the other fruits).

FAT: 1G (1%) • PROTEIN: 2G (4%) • CARBOHYDRATE: 68G (23%) • FIBRE: 5G (20%)
VITAMIN A: 70% • VITAMIN C: 170% • VITAMIN K: 100% • CHOLESTEROL: 0

Rhubarb and Plum Tart

Another cholesterol-free dessert which, as well as helping to protect your heart, can aid digestion, relieve constipation and support the liver. Rhubarb, which also has anti-cancer properties, has been shown to stimulate uterine contractions and has been used to regulate menstruation. Plums are a natural laxative; antiviral and antibacterial, they also help strengthen the immune system and keep infections at bay.

SERVES 6

800g (1lb 12oz) rhubarb

200g (7oz) plums, stoned and halved

250g (9oz) brown sugar

60ml (2fl oz) water

300g (10½oz) puff pastry

100g (3½oz) apricot jam

2 tbsp rum

1 Wash, drain and strip the stringy edges from the rhubarb stalks. Cut each one into 2cm (1in) lengths. Place the rhubarb, plums, brown sugar and water in an ovenproof dish, cover with foil and cook for 15 minutes in a preheated oven (220°C/425°F/Gas 7). Leave to cool.

2 Roll the puff pastry as thinly as possible and shape into a round. Use to line a 25cm (10in) tart tin. Prick with a fork.

3 Cover the base with the rhubarb and plum mixture and bake for 25 minutes in a preheated oven (200°C/400°F/Gas 6). When the tart is cooked, melt the apricot jam with the rum and pour over the top of the tart to glaze it.

For a special occasion, pour cold custard over the pastry base of the tart before piling on the fruit and cooking. (This will make the tart higher in fat.) You can also cook the rhubarb with other fruits; try apricot or peach.

FAT: 20G (30%) • PROTEIN: 5G (10%) • CARBOHYDRATE: 85G (28%) • FIBRE: 4G (15%)
VITAMIN C: 25% • POTASSIUM: 70% • CHOLESTEROL: 10%

The**A-Team**

SERVES 4

CIABATTA BREAD WITH ROASTED VEGETABLES AND MOZZARELLA, VEGETABLE CRISPS AND A CRUNCHY CRANBERRY BAR

Packed with almost six times the minimum daily requirement of immune-boosting, cancer-fighting vitamin A, and almost three times the minimum amount of vitamin C you need to keep disease at bay, this picnic will help fight cancers, increase immunity, banish stress and give you more energy.

② ③ ❹ ⑤ ⑥ ❽ ❾ ⑩

The Sandwich

1 onion, quartered	1 sprig of fresh oregano
2 large carrots, cut into chunks	4 cherry tomatoes
1 red pepper, deseeded and quartered	3 sprigs of fresh thyme
1 green pepper, quartered	freshly ground black pepper
2 small courgettes, cut into chunks	2 tbsp balsamic vinegar
6 garlic cloves, skins left on	4 x mini ciabatta bread
100ml (3½fl oz) olive oil	100g (3½oz) mozzarella, sliced
	8 fresh basil leaves

1 In a large bowl, mix the vegetables with the garlic, olive oil, oregano, tomatoes and thyme. Season. Pile all this onto a baking tray and cook in a preheated oven (220°C/425°F/Gas 7) for 25 minutes.

2 Remove from the oven, add the vinegar and leave to cool. Now cut all the vegetables small enough to be eaten in a sandwich. Cut each ciabatta bread in half. Fill with the sliced mozzarella, chilled roasted vegetables and fresh basil leaves.

FAT: 30G (46%) • PROTEIN: 15G (30%) • CARBOHYDRATE: 50G (17%)
FIBRE: 7G (27%) • VITAMIN A: 450% • VITAMIN C: 170% • CALCIUM: 30%
CHOLESTEROL: 5%

The Crisps

2 courgettes	2 raw beetroot, peeled
3 carrots, peeled	freshly ground black pepper
3 parsnips, peeled	
3 potatoes, peeled	

1 Slice the courgettes lengthways into long, thin strips. Use a potato peeler to shave all the vegetables into slivers, trying to make the slivers as wide as you can because they will curl.

2 Place all the shavings on a baking tray which you have lined with greaseproof paper and dry-roast them in the oven on its lowest setting until they look like crisps (about 15 minutes). Season to taste.

FAT: 0.5G (1%) • PROTEIN: 5G (10%) • CARBOHYDRATE: 41G (14%)
FIBRE: 8G (34%) • VITAMIN A: 210% • VITAMIN C: 70% • POTASSIUM: 140%
CHOLESTEROL: 0

Cranberry Bar

125g (4½oz) demerara sugar	125g (4½oz) soya flour
1 tbsp golden syrup	125g (4½oz) oat flakes
125g (4½oz) olive oil spread	50g (1¾oz) dried cranberries

1 Put the sugar, golden syrup and olive oil spread in a pan and melt gently over a low heat. When melted, add all the other ingredients and mix well.

2 Cover a flat tin with greaseproof paper and pour the mixture in. Cook in an oven preheated to (180°C/350°F/Gas 4) for 15–20 minutes. Leave to cool and slice into ten picnic bars.

You can replace the cranberries with any other kind of dried fruits, for example figs or prunes.

FAT: 9G (14%) • PROTEIN: 7G (14%) • CARBOHYDRATE: 26G (9%)
FIBRE: 3G (13%) • VITAMIN A: 8% • VITAMIN E: 10% • IRON: 10%
CHOLESTEROL: 0

The **B-Team**

SERVES 4

PUMPKIN BREAD WITH AVOCADO, WATERCRESS AND WALNUTS, CARROT AND PECAN NUT SALAD AND CHARENTAIS MELON BALLS

This power-packed picnic is full of the all-important B vitamins, without which not much happens in the body. B vitamins help maintain healthy skin, nerves, digestion, reproductive system, blood, circulation and brainpower. Pumpkin seeds are rich in prostate-protecting zinc, bone-building calcium and B vitamins.

① ② ③ ④ ⑤ ⑥ ⑧ ⑩

The Salad

400g (14oz) carrots, grated	**100g (3½oz) mango, diced**
juice of 1 lemon	**80g (3oz) sultanas**
juice of 1 orange	**90ml (3fl oz) olive oil**
100g (3½oz) pecan nuts, roasted	**1 tbsp chopped fresh chives**

1 Mix all the ingredients except the chives together and chill for at least 2 hours before you want to pack it. Sprinkle with chopped chives and eat.

FAT: 35G (54%) • PROTEIN: 4G (8%) • CARBOHYDRATE: 38G (13%)
FIBRE: 7G (30%) • VITAMIN A: 580% • POTASSIUM: 71% • CHOLESTEROL: 0

Melon Balls

1 large Charentais melon	**10 fresh mint leaves**

1 Cut and deseed the melon. Use a melon baller to scoop the flesh out and mix with the chopped mint. Chill in a cool box before eating.

FAT: 0G (0%) • PROTEIN: 1G (2%) • CARBOHYDRATE: 14G (5%) • FIBRE: LESS
THAN 1G (4%) • VITAMIN C: 60% • POTASSIUM: 45% • CHOLESTEROL: 0

The Sandwich

225g (8oz) pumpkin, diced		*For the filling:*
1 tsp sugar		**2 ripe avocados, sliced**
5 tsp warm soya milk, plus extra to glaze		**juice of 1 lemon**
15g (½oz) dried yeast		**1 bunch of watercress, roughly chopped**
225g (8oz) wholemeal flour (use gluten-free if intolerant)		**50g (1¾oz) walnuts**
½ tsp cinnamon		**15g (½oz) pumpkin seeds, roasted**
½ tsp ground ginger		**4 tsp olive oil**
1 pinch of freshly grated nutmeg		**freshly ground black pepper**
20g (¾oz) olive oil spread		**50g (1¾oz) olive oil spread**
2 tsp salt		
20g (¾oz) pumpkin seeds		

1 To make the pumpkin bread, cook the pumpkin in boiling water until tender. Drain and purée. Combine the sugar, milk and yeast together in a bowl. Leave to stand for 10 minutes.

2 In another large bowl, mix the flour, spices, olive oil spread and salt. Create a well in the middle and pour the yeast mixture and the puréed pumpkin into it. Use a knife to mix all the ingredients together lightly and then transfer to a well-floured surface.

3 Begin to knead the dough, adding more flour if too wet. Knead for at least 5 minutes and, when the dough is smooth, return to the bowl and leave it to double in size. Return it to your floured worktop, knead for 2–3 minutes then shape into a ball. Place on a baking tray, cover and leave to double in size in a warm place.

4 When ready, glaze the dough with milk and sprinkle pumpkin seeds on top. Bake in a preheated oven (200°C/400°F/Gas 6) for 30 minutes. When cooked, take the bread out of the oven, brush the top with milk and return to the oven for another 10 minutes until the top is shiny and crusty. Leave to cool.

5 To make the sandwich, arrange the avocados so they lie flat in a dish. Squeeze the lemon juice over the top to stop them from blackening. Add the watercress to the avocados along with the walnuts, pumpkin seeds and olive oil.

6 Season to taste and leave to chill for 5 minutes. Slice the pumpkin bread, top with the olive oil spread and pile on the filling.

FAT: 53G (81%) • PROTEIN: 10G (20%) • CARBOHYDRATE: 73G (24%)
FIBRE: 7G (30%) • VITAMIN B3: 48% • VITAMIN B6: 25% • CALCIUM: 6%
FOLATE: 21% • ZINC: 10% • CHOLESTEROL: 18%

The**San-Fran** Special

SERVES 4

SAN FRANCISCO BAGELS WITH CREAM CHEESE,
DILL AND SMOKED SALMON,
MINI STUFFED VINE LEAVES AND FRESH FIGS

The so-called oily fish, which include salmon, are a good source of vitamins A and D and are rich in the omega-3 fatty acids that help lower cholesterol and high blood pressure. Researchers have also found a link between increased rates of depression and a decline in the consumption of oily fish. Omega-3s are fragile substances that can be destroyed by heat, but in this picnic meal, the salmon is smoked rather than cooked, so this is clearly not a problem. Thanks to the figs, which are high in fibre, this picnic also has an anti-cancer action.

② ③ ④ ⑦ ⑧ ⑩

The Bagel

4 x bagels

250g (9oz) low-fat cream cheese

2 tbsp chopped fresh dill

freshly ground black pepper

4 slices smoked salmon

1 Slice the bagels in two and toast to a golden brown. Mix the cream cheese with the dill and season to taste.
2 Cut the salmon into 5mm (¼ in) wide strips. Fill the bagels with the cream cheese and smoked salmon.

FAT: 14G (22%) • PROTEIN: 24G (48%) • CARBOHYDRATE: 42G (14%)
FIBRE: 2G (7%) • VITAMIN A: 10% • VITAMIN D: 80% • CALCIUM: 15% • FOLATE: 18%
IRON: 20% • CHOLESTEROL: 10%

The Stuffed Vine Leaves

1 large onion, diced

3 garlic cloves, crushed

50ml (2fl oz) olive oil

1 large aubergine, peeled and diced

25g (1oz) sun-dried tomatoes, diced

200g (7oz) brown rice

500ml (18fl oz) vegetable stock

½ tsp ground turmeric

freshly ground black pepper

50g (1¾oz) Feta cheese, diced

25g (1oz) pitted black olives, chopped

50g (1¾oz) fresh flat-leaved parsley, chopped

2 tbsp balsamic vinegar

12 vine leaves (in brine)

1 Cook the onion and garlic in the olive oil for 10 minutes until tender but not browned. Add the diced aubergine and sun-dried tomatoes and cook for another 5 minutes. Add the rice and stir to coat every grain.
2 Add the stock and the ground turmeric and season. Cover and cook on a low heat for 20 minutes or until the liquid has evaporated and the rice is tender. Add the Feta cheese, olives and chopped parsley and leave to cool.
3 When the rice is cold, mix in the vinegar and check the seasoning. Lay the vine leaves out, one at a time, on a work surface and place a tablespoonful of the filling at the bottom of each leaf. Roll up the leaf tightly to create a mini parcel. Do this with all 12 leaves and chill in the refrigerator until you are ready to pack your picnic lunch. Pack with the bagels and fresh figs.

FAT: 17G (27%) • PROTEIN: 9G (18%) • CARBOHYDRATE: 54G (18%)
FIBRE: 5G (20%) • VITAMIN A: 25% • VITAMIN C: 30% • POTASSIUM: 71%
CHOLESTEROL: 4%

The Fresh Figs

8 fresh figs

FAT: 0 • PROTEIN: 1G (2%) • CARBOHYDRATE: 19G (6%) • FIBRE: 3G (13%)
VITAMIN C: 4% • POTASSIUM: 26% • CHOLESTEROL: 0

InA**Nutshell**

SERVES 4

WHOLEMEAL PITTA WITH HOMEMADE HUMMUS AND VEGETABLE SALAD, BUTTER BEAN, PASTA AND BRAZIL NUT SALAD AND BANANA AND ALMOND WHEAT-FREE MUFFIN

With brazil nuts, sesame seed paste, chickpeas, almonds and butter beans, this fibre-packed picnic will help protect against colon cancer, which is rapidly becoming the biggest killer in developed countries. It also combats digestive disorders such as irritable bowel syndrome, which is becoming a modern-day scourge: more working days are lost to IBS than to back pain, for example.

① ② ③ ⑤ **❽** ⑩

The Sandwich

100g (3½oz) carrots, grated	**200g (7oz) hummus (see below)**
100g (3½oz) red cabbage, grated	
80g (3oz) lettuce, shredded	*For the hummus:*
80g (3oz) celery, finely sliced	**400g (14oz) chickpeas, soaked**
80g (3oz) cucumber, finely sliced	**1 onion, diced**
	4 garlic cloves, crushed
2 tbsp chopped fresh flat-leaved parsley	**80g (3oz) tahini (sesame seed paste)**
freshly ground black pepper	**juice of 3 lemons**
	1 pinch paprika
4 wholemeal pitta breads	**1 tbsp chopped fresh parsley**

1 To make the hummus, cook the soaked chickpeas for 3–4 hours, skimming the surface scum off the water. When cooked, drain and transfer to a food processor. Add the onion, garlic and tahini, and blend until smooth.
2 Finish with lemon juice and season to taste. Chill thoroughly and serve with paprika and chopped parsley sprinkled on top.
3 To make the pitta sandwich, mix all the vegetables with the parsley and season to taste. Toast the pitta breads, slice them open and spread a generous layer of home-made hummus inside. Pack each one full of the vegetable mix and wrap individually ready for the picnic.

FAT: 6G (9%) • PROTEIN: 10G (20%) • CARBOHYDRATE: 51G (17%)
FIBRE: 9G (37%) • VITAMIN A: 150% • VITAMIN C: 45% • CHOLESTEROL: 0

The Salad

300g (10½oz) butter beans, soaked	**100g (3½oz) brazil nuts, chopped**
1 pinch of turmeric	**5 tbsp chopped fresh coriander**
200g (7oz) wholewheat pasta	**juice of 2 limes**
1 red pepper, diced	**60ml (2fl oz) olive oil**
1 onion, finely sliced	**freshly ground black pepper**

1 Cook the butter beans with the turmeric for at least 2 hours until tender and drain. Cook the pasta in boiling water and drain.
2 Mix the beans and pasta with the pepper, onion, brazil nuts, coriander, lime juice and olive oil, reserving a little coriander to garnish. Season and serve very cold, garnished with chopped coriander.

FAT: 29G (45%) • PROTEIN: 12G (24%) • CARBOHYDRATE: 35G (12%)
FIBRE: 9G (35%) • VITAMIN C: 100% • IRON: 20% • CHOLESTEROL: 0

The Muffin

300g (10½oz) rice flour	**250ml (9fl oz) soya milk**
15g (½oz) baking powder	**2 drops vanilla essence**
2 tbsp Muscovado sugar	**50g (1¾oz) semi-dried banana**
1 pinch of salt	
50g (1¾oz) margarine	**20g (¾oz) almonds, chopped**
1 egg, beaten	

1 Mix the rice flour, baking powder and sugar with a pinch of salt. Add the margarine, beaten egg, soya milk and vanilla essence and stir until mixed but not too smooth.
2 Dice the semi-dried bananas and add them to the batter with the chopped almonds. Pour this mixture into a muffin pan until it is two-thirds full. Cook for 25 minutes in a preheated oven (190°C/375°F/Gas 5).
3 When cooked, leave to cool and, when cold, pack in air-tight containers ready for your picnic lunch.

FAT: 14G (21%) • PROTEIN: 7G (14%) • CARBOHYDRATE: 60G (20%)
FIBRE: 4G (15%) • VITAMIN E: 25% • CALCIUM: 20% • POTASSIUM: 45%
CHOLESTEROL: 10%

Lunchbox**Spice**

SERVES 4

GRANARY BREAD WITH STIR-FRIED CHICKEN
AND WATER CHESTNUTS, SPICY AIOLI CROÛTONS
AND BLACKBERRY SHORTCAKE

Turn back the clock with this anti-ageing, anti-cancer lunch
that contains high levels of selenium as well as plenty of
calcium and folate. Selenium is crucial for the manufacture
of glutathione peroxidase, the body's main antioxidant,
which is found in every single cell. In some trials, people
taking regular doses of selenium were half as likely to die
from cancer than those who did not take the mineral.
Researchers now believe selenium plays a purely
preventative role, stopping cancer from
developing in the first place.

① ③ ❹ ⑤ ⑥ ❽ ⑩

The Sandwich

**300g (10½oz) chicken,
cut into strips**

**4 tsp sesame oil
(or olive oil)**

¼ tsp Chinese five spice

2 tbsp soy sauce

**20g (¾oz) sesame seeds,
toasted**

1 spring onion, chopped

4 tsp rice vinegar

**800g (1lb 12oz) water
chestnuts, sliced**

8 slices granary bread

1 Sauté the chicken strips in the sesame oil for 2 minutes.
Add the Chinese five spice, soy sauce and sesame seeds.
Cook for another 5–6 minutes, put to one side and leave
to cool.
2 In a mixing bowl, combine the cooked chicken with the
spring onion, rice vinegar and the water chestnuts. Fill
your sandwiches with this delicious mix and store in an
airtight container.

FAT: 10G (15%) • PROTEIN: 8G (16%) • CARBOHYDRATE: 36G (12%)
FIBRE: 5G (21%) • IRON: 15% • SELENIUM: 41% • CHOLESTEROL: 0

The Croûtons

**2 large potatoes,
cut into chunks**

6 garlic cloves

½ tsp turmeric

1 egg, beaten

250ml (9fl oz) olive oil

juice of 1 lemon

**freshly ground black
pepper**

1 French baguette

1 Cook the potato chunks in water until tender. Drain. Put
the garlic cloves in a saucepan of cold water, bring to the
boil and drain. Repeat this procedure twice more to blanch
the cloves.
2 In a food processor, blend the potatoes, turmeric, egg and
blanched garlic, and after 10 seconds drizzle in the olive
oil, little by little, as if making mayonnaise. Add the lemon
juice, check the seasoning and put the dish to one side.
3 Cut the baguette into 2.5cm (1in) thick slices, spread the
aioli sauce on the top, cut in quarters and place on a
baking tray in a preheated oven (150°C/300°F/Gas 2) until
the bread is dry and crispy. Leave to cool and store in an
airtight container.

FAT: 40G (61%) • PROTEIN: 3G (6%) • CARBOHYDRATE: 13G (4%)
FIBRE: 1G (5%) • VITAMIN C: 20% • CALCIUM: 2% • IRON: 4% • CHOLESTEROL: 12%

The Shortcake

**300g (10½oz) flour
(or wheat-free)**

25g (1oz) Muscovado sugar

1 pinch of salt

25g (1oz) baking powder

80g (3oz) soya spread

160ml (5¼fl oz) soya milk

200g (7oz) blackberries

**300g (10½oz) low-fat
fromage frais**

1 In a large bowl, mix the flour and sugar with a pinch of
salt and the baking powder. Add the soya spread to the
flour and mix it all gently with your fingers. Slowly add the
milk to create a dough.
2 Flour the worktop and work the dough for 2 minutes.
Transfer to a cake tin and cook in a preheated oven
(200°C/400°F/Gas 6) for 15 minutes.
3 When cool, carefully split the cake in two, horizontally.
Mix the blackberries with the fromage frais and spread this
mixture between the two layers of shortcake.

FAT: 12G (19%) • PROTEIN: 12G (24%) • CARBOHYDRATE: 51G (17%)
FIBRE: 2G (9%) • CALCIUM: 30% • FOLATE: 21% • CHOLESTEROL: 0

Fruit-Packed**Treat**

SERVES 4

RYE BREAD WITH HAM, CELERY AND APPLES,
CAJUN-ROASTED POTATO WEDGES AND
HONEY, FIG AND NUT BAR

It's true that an apple a day really will keep the doctor away, although if you want to guarantee not to see him, try eating 2–3 a day for maximum health benefits. Apples have a multitude of nutritional properties. That means they can reduce cholesterol, fight bacteria and viruses, combat cancer, reduce menopausal symptoms and boost the cardiovascular system. Full of soluble fibre, apples can also aid weight loss: eat one before a main meal to reduce your appetite. The other fruit in this healthy picnic are figs, which are not only delicious, they have also been shown to help reduce cancer tumours.

① ② ③ ④ ⑧ ⑩

The Potato Wedges

4 baking potatoes	50ml (2fl oz) olive oil
2 tsp Cajun spice	

1 Cut the potatoes into thin wedges. Mix them with the Cajun spice and the olive oil and bake on a baking tray in a preheated oven (200°C/400°F/Gas 6) for 25–30 minutes until golden and crispy. Season to taste and eat with different dips such as hummus (*see page 126*).

FAT: 12G (18%) • PROTEIN: 4G (8%) • CARBOHYDRATE: 45G (15%)
FIBRE: 4G (17%) • VITAMIN C: 40% • POTASSIUM: 83% • CHOLESTEROL: 0

The Sandwich

8 slices rye bread	freshly ground black pepper
50g (1¾oz) olive oil spread	
4 slices cooked ham	100g (3½oz) celery, chopped
1 large apple, peeled, cored and sliced	

1 Spread the rye bread with the olive oil spread and fill your sandwiches with sliced ham, sliced apples and celery.

FAT: 16G (24%) • PROTEIN: 16G (32%) • CARBOHYDRATE: 39G (13%)
FIBRE: 5G (21%) • VITAMIN B3: 35% • FOLATE: 17% • IRON: 15%
CHOLESTEROL: 10%

The Honey and Fig Bar

25g (1oz) soya spread	½ tsp baking powder
100g (3½oz) dried diced figs	100g (3½oz) honey
25g (1oz) hazelnuts	1 tsp vanilla essence
25g (1oz) pistachios	2 eggs, beaten
100g (3½oz) white flour (or wheat-free)	25g (1oz) peanuts

1 Melt the soya spread and mix with the other ingredients. Line a baking tray with greaseproof paper then pour in the mixture. Spread evenly and cook in a preheated oven (180°C/350°F/Gas 4) for 20–25 minutes until it is firm to the touch and golden.
2 Leave to cool for 10 minutes, then cut into even-sized bars. When completely cold, wrap them individually and keep sealed in an airtight container.

FAT: 12G (19%) • PROTEIN: 6G (12%) • CARBOHYDRATE: 31G (10%)
FIBRE: 4G (17%) • IRON: 10% • POTASSIUM: 29% • SELENIUM: 18%
CHOLESTEROL: 18%

COOKING FOR HEALTHY KIDS

Polenta Pizza Faces

Children need, proportionately, higher levels of carbohydrates compared with adults. A shortage causes lethargy, exhaustion and the breakdown of proteins needed to make strong muscles in the body. As well as providing plenty of carbohydrates, these healthy pizzas are also an excellent source of calcium for growing bones, of iron, which is needed to make red blood cells and build resistance to disease, and of vitamin C, which enhances iron absorption.

MAKES 8 ① ❹ ⑤ ⑥ ⑩

For the polenta base:

1.5 litres (2¼ pints) water

180g (6¼oz) quick-cook polenta

For the tomato sauce:

2 large onions, chopped

3 garlic cloves, crushed

60ml (2fl oz) olive oil

1.5kg (3lb 5oz) tomatoes, skinned, deseeded and chopped

50g (1¾oz) tomato purée

1 pinch sugar

2 bay leaves

1 sprig fresh oregano

freshly ground black pepper

For the faces:

100g (3½oz) mozzarella cheese, grated

16 black olives, pitted

1 red pepper, cut into strips

1 Cook the onion and garlic in the olive oil for 5 minutes, then add the other sauce ingredients. Cook gently until most of the water has evaporated.
2 Bring the water to the boil. Add the polenta and stir constantly for 7 minutes. Transfer the polenta to an oiled tray (use olive oil) and leave to cool.
3 When cold, use a 6cm (2½in) round pastry cutter to cut the polenta into eight circles. Place them on a baking tray and cover with the sauce.
4 Make a face with the black olives for eyes and the strips of red pepper for mouths. Top with the grated mozzarella and grill until the cheese has melted and the polenta is heated through. Serve with a green salad.

FAT: 11G (16%) • PROTEIN: 13G (44%) • CARBOHYDRATE: 48G (16%)
FIBRE: 6G (29%) • VITAMIN C: 146% • CALCIUM: 34% • IRON: 26%
CHOLESTEROL: 2%

Home-made Bulgarian-style Yogurt

Keep your child's heart, muscles, kidneys and blood healthy with this simple but important dish, which is a good source of calcium and, unlike so many supermarket brands, is not processed with sugar or polluted with additives. The folate will help maintain healthy hair and skin and is also good for the nervous system. The selenium supports the pancreas and helps the body to make better use of vitamin E and build resistance to all cancers.

MAKES 4 ① ❹ ⑤ ⑧

500ml (18fl oz) semi-skimmed organic milk (use soya milk if preferred)

1 sachet of Bulgarian-style yogurt culture or similar, from your healthfood shop

1 Bring the milk to the boil, then leave to cool until just warm. Add the yogurt culture (follow the instructions on the packet) and mix well. Sterilize a large glass bowl by pouring boiling water over it.
2 Transfer the warm milk to the bowl, cover with cling film and leave to rest for 8 hours until set. Keep in the refrigerator. Eat with the Quick Confiture of Guava (or Pineapple) *(see page 114)*.

Remember to reserve one tablespoon in order to make your next batch of yogurt.

FAT: 1.9G (3%) • PROTEIN: 6.43G (22%) • CARBOHYDRATE: 8.62G (3%)
CALCIUM: 28% • FOLATE: 7% • POTASSIUM: 14% • SELENIUM: 13%
CHOLESTEROL: 2%

Nutcase Burgers with Tomato Sauce

This tasty meal provides at least half the recommended daily allowance of all the minerals your child needs to stay fit and well, as well as plenty of vitamin C which regulates the normal functioning of the enzymes responsible for growth. Vitamin C also accelerates wound-healing, which is important for kids who are always in the wars, and helps immune systems besieged by childhood bugs. This recipe is packed with iron supplies and just goes to show that choosing the right type of burgers can be a healthy choice!

SERVES 4   ① ② ④ ⑤

250g (9oz) cauliflower, cut into florets	50g (1¾oz) pumpkin seeds
2 large onions, finely diced	50g (1¾oz) sunflower seeds, roasted
2 garlic cloves, crushed	100g (3½oz) flour
60ml (2fl oz) olive oil	2 eggs, beaten
1 tsp paprika	125g (4½oz) breadcrumbs
50g (1¾oz) almonds, chopped	400ml (14fl oz) tomato sauce (see sauce recipe for Polenta Pizza Faces, page 132)
50g (1¾oz) pecan nuts, chopped	

1 Cook the cauliflower in boiling water until very tender. Drain well, transfer to a food processor and blend until smooth. Cook the onion and garlic in olive oil for 10 minutes until tender, but not discoloured.
2 In a large bowl, combine the cauliflower with the paprika, chopped nuts, seeds, onions and garlic. Form into round burger shapes and coat first in the flour, then in the beaten eggs and finally in the breadcrumbs.
3 Cook the burgers on a barbecue or griddle, with a little olive oil on both sides, until golden. Serve with tomato sauce and healthy brown rice.

FAT: 20G (29%) • PROTEIN: 11G (38%) • CARBOHYDRATE: 35G (11%)
FIBRE: 10G (48%) • VITAMIN C: 138% • FOLATE: 82% • IRON: 54%
CHOLESTEROL: 36%

Raspberry Rice Pudding

Another calcium-rich dish for growing kids, this is also high in potassium, which helps transfer nutrients through the cell membranes. Of all grains, rice is the most easily digested and the least likely to cause allergic reactions. It can help clear psoriasis. The red raspberries in the accompanying compote are good for healthy skin, nails, bones and teeth and can help relieve stomach upsets.

SERVES 4   ② ③ ④ ⑥

200g (7oz) short-grain pudding rice	4 fresh mint leaves
1 litre (1¾ pints) organic milk (or use soya milk)	*For the raspberry compote:*
½ tsp vanilla essence	100g (3½oz) fresh raspberries
80g (3oz) sugar	25g (1oz) sugar
2 egg yolks, beaten	5 tsp water
60ml (2fl oz) almond cream	

1 Bring some water to the boil in a large saucepan and cook the rice for just 3 minutes to blanch it. Drain the rice, and then boil the milk with the vanilla essence, sugar and drained rice until all the milk has evaporated and the rice is swollen with the liquid.
2 Off the heat, stir in the beaten egg yolks and the almond cream. Stir quickly to stop the heat of the rice cooking the egg yolks. Put on one side to cool.
3 To make the compote, put all the raspberries except four in a small pan with the sugar and water. Cook gently on the hob for 10 minutes. Pour some compote into the bottom of each of four ramekin dishes and cover with the creamy rice. Leave to cool completely. Decorate with the reserved raspberries and mint leaves.

For a thicker rice pudding, increase the amount of rice you cook by 50g (1¾oz). You can also substitute caramel sauce for the compote.

FAT: 12G (17%) • PROTEIN: 12G (40%) • CARBOHYDRATE: 56G (20%)
FIBRE: 2G (11%) • CALCIUM: 41% • FOLATE: 30% • POTASSIUM: 23%
CHOLESTEROL: 47%

Chicken Pasty with Green Basil Sauce

Although this recipe looks high in fat, only 19 of the 83 fat grams are saturated. The chicken is packed with iron and B vitamins and the tasty green basil sauce helps stimulate the immune system.

SERVES 4　　　① ② ③ ❹ ❻ ❽

For the pasty:

500g (1lb 2oz) wholemeal flour

200g (7oz) white flour

1 pinch of salt

175g (6oz) olive oil spread

175g (6oz) vegetable shortening

125ml (4fl oz) water

3 chicken breasts, skinless, finely diced

1 carrot, grated

1 bulb of fennel, sliced

2 tbsp chicken stock

3 medium tomatoes, skinned and deseeded

freshly ground black pepper

80g (3oz) mozzarella cheese, grated

1 egg yolk

For the basil sauce:

50g (1¾oz) olive oil spread

50g (1¾oz) flour

250ml (9fl oz) chicken stock

50g (1¾oz) fresh parsley, chopped

80ml (3fl oz) soya cream

5 basil leaves, chopped

1 For the pastry, sift the flours, then mix in the salt, olive oil spread and vegetable shortening until the mixture resembles breadcrumbs. Make a well in the centre and add water to make a firm paste; handle this as little as possible. Wrap in clingfilm and refrigerate for 1 hour.

2 Mix the chicken with the carrot, fennel and chicken stock. Chop the tomatoes and add the seasoning. Roll the dough to 3mm (⅛in) thickness. Use a 19cm (7½in) pastry cutter to make four discs; divide the chicken mixture between them. Sprinkle mozzarella on top of each filling.

3 Brush the edges of each disc with water and fold over, to make a pasty shape. Place on a greased baking tray and brush with a mix of water and egg yolk. Bake at 190°C/375°F/Gas 5 for 30–40 minutes.

4 To make the sauce, melt the spread in a saucepan, add the flour and cook for 2 minutes, whisking constantly. Add the chicken stock and bring gently to the boil. Cook for another 2–3 minutes until the sauce thickens, then stir in the parsley, cream and basil. Season and serve the pasties with vegetables and green sauce.

FAT: 83G (120%) • PROTEIN: 42G (142%) • CARBOHYDRATE: 143G (48%)
FIBRE: 21G (100%) • VITAMIN B3: 200% • VITAMIN C: 95% • FOLATE: 94%
IRON: 94% • CHOLESTEROL: 36%

Date-stuffed Baked Apples with Honey

Tiredness, irritability and sleeplessness are all signs of vitamin B3 (niacin) deficiency, which this recipe combats. As well as maintaining a healthy nervous system, vitamin B3 helps regulate hormones, and so is particularly important for teenagers. Dates, which have a delicious, natural sweetness, help keep the digestion healthy.

SERVES 4　　　② ③ ❹ ⑤ ⑥ ⑩

4 large cooking apples

35g (1¼oz) almonds, blanched and chopped

60g (2oz) dried dates, chopped

4 tbsp honey

4 cloves

35g (1¼oz) soya spread

1 Core the apples and, a third of the way down from the top, pierce the skins and make an incision, no more than 2mm into the flesh, around the whole circumference of each apple.

2 Arrange in a baking dish that is sufficiently deep to hold enough water to cover the bottom 1cm (½in) of the apples. In the centre of each apple, where you have removed the core, fill with almonds, dates, honey, a clove and the soya spread, in that order. Pour warm water into the bottom of the tray.

3 Bake in a preheated oven (200°C/400°F/Gas 6) for 15 minutes. Then, turn each apple upside down, and cook for another 30–35 minutes. Serve the apples with hot custard or vanilla ice cream.

FAT: 12G (17%) • PROTEIN: 3G (10%) • CARBOHYDRATE: 63G (21%)
FIBRE: 8G (39%) • VITAMIN B3: 20% • VITAMIN C: 27% • POTASSIUM: 21%
CHOLESTEROL: 0

Popeye's Fat Jacket Potatoes

Although spinach can inhibit the full absorption of calcium, it is full of goodness and helps boost levels of other nutrients, so it should be included in some of your children's meals. In small doses, nutmeg, a very calming herb, improves the appetite – which makes it helpful for faddy eaters. Nutmeg also aids the digestion.

SERVES 4 ① ② ③ ④ ⑤ ⑥ ⑧

4 large baking potatoes

300g (10½oz) rock salt (not consumed)

25g (1oz) soya spread

25g (1oz) white flour

300ml (½ pint) milk

50g (1¾oz) Feta cheese

1 egg yolk, beaten

½ tsp nutmeg

freshly ground black pepper

1 large bunch of fresh spinach, chopped

400g (14oz) boneless, cooked chicken meat, diced

1 Wash the potatoes and place them on a baking tray that has been covered in rock salt. The salt absorbs the humidity, giving a crispier skin. Cook for at least 1 hour in a preheated oven (180°C/350°F/Gas 4) until the potatoes feel soft when you squeeze them.

2 Meanwhile, prepare the white sauce. Melt the soya spread, add the flour and cook over a gentle heat for 2–3 minutes, whisking all the time. Add the milk, stirring constantly, and bring to the boil.

3 Cook for another 2–3 minutes, until the sauce thickens. Whisk to avoid lumps. Off the heat, add the Feta cheese, beaten egg yolk and nutmeg. Season.

4 Cook the chopped spinach with a little water, stirring occasionally, until it wilts. Remove from the heat and season.

5 In a large bowl, combine the diced chicken meat, white sauce and the wilted spinach to make the filling.

6 When the potatoes are ready, slice in half, lengthways, scoop out all the flesh without piercing the skin, and mix with the filling. Fill each potato skin with this mixture and be generous. Lightly brown the tops of the potatoes under the grill. Serve with green French beans.

FAT: 22G (32%) • PROTEIN: 41G (138%) • CARBOHYDRATE: 33G (11%)
FIBRE: 4G (17%) • VITAMIN A: 141% • FOLATE: 136% • POTASSIUM: 70%
CHOLESTEROL: 55%

Chocolate and Ginger Ice Cream

The best thing about home-made ice cream is that you know exactly what has gone into it and do not have to rely on a frequently misleading label to work out either the true fat and sugar content or which horrible additives have been used. Ginger, which is very good for relieving nausea and travel sickness, stimulates all the body's tissues, is very warming and often helps where illness is a result of poor assimilation of nutrients.

SERVES 6 ① ② ④ ⑥

70g (2½oz) caster sugar

6 egg yolks

500ml (17fl oz) soya milk

90g (3oz) good quality cooking chocolate, grated

2 stems of ginger, finely diced

2 vanilla pods, split in half lengthways

1 To make the custard, beat the sugar and egg yolks in a large bowl until they are white and fluffy. Bring the milk, grated chocolate, diced ginger and vanilla pods to the boil and then pour gently onto the sugar and egg mixture, whisking constantly.

2 Transfer this mixture back to the saucepan and cook very gently, stirring with a metal spoon, until the custard coats the back of the spoon. Remove from the heat and pour into a bowl to cool.

3 Place the chilled custard in a metal container and put in the freezer. Leave it to harden, but whisk every 20 minutes until ready. When ready to eat, scoop out the ice cream and serve with chocolate flakes and (for adults) grated stem ginger on top.

FAT: 14G (20%) • PROTEIN: 6G (22%) • CARBOHYDRATE: 25G (8%)
FIBRE: 3G (15%) • VITAMIN A: 14% • IRON: 37% • POTASSIUM: 23%
CHOLESTEROL: 71%

Green Risotto Galettes

This recipe, which cleverly disguises organic vegetables, is a storehouse of antioxidants – especially of betacarotenes, which help prevent cancer. Betacarotenes are converted in the body to Vitamin A, which helps the body to make better use of nutrients and boosts the immune system, helping to produce antibodies. Vitamin A is needed by all the cells in the body and, as well as promoting healthy skin, nails, hair and bones, it will speed recovery from illness.

SERVES 4   ① ③ ⑤ ⑥ ⑧ ⑨

1 large onion, finely diced

2 garlic cloves, crushed

90ml (3fl oz) olive oil

75g (2¾oz) courgettes, grated

75g (2¾oz) carrots, grated

300g (10½oz) Arborio rice

900ml (1½ pints) vegetable stock

70g (2½oz) cooked peas

2 large tomatoes, skinned, deseeded and chopped

freshly ground black pepper

50g (1¾oz) fresh Parmesan cheese, grated

5 tbsp chopped fresh parsley

2 eggs, beaten

80g (3oz) polenta flour

1 In a large pan, cook the diced onion and garlic in half of the olive oil for 5 minutes, until tender. Add the grated courgettes and carrots and cook for another 5 minutes.

2 Add the Arborio rice and cook for 2 minutes, stirring to coat every grain. Begin slowly to add some of the hot vegetable stock, stirring all the time.

3 After about 10 minutes, add the peas and tomatoes. Season and add the rest of the stock a ladleful at a time, stirring continuously, until the rice is cooked: it should be puffed and creamy. Now add the Parmesan cheese and the chopped parsley and leave to cool.

4 When the rice is cold, form eight small round flat cakes (like fishcakes). Dip each one in the beaten egg and roll in polenta flour. Cook the galettes in the remaining olive oil until each side is golden and the rice in the centre of each cake is heated through. Serve with green salad leaves.

FAT: 25G (37%) • PROTEIN: 18G (60%) • CARBOHYDRATE: 85G (28%)
FIBRE: 5G (25%) • VITAMIN A: 100% • VITAMIN C: 87% • CALCIUM: 32%
CHOLESTEROL: 34%

Cranberry and Raspberry Jelly

This immune-boosting jelly will give your children a blast of vitamin C to help keep coughs, colds and other bugs at bay – and whoever imagined a simple jelly could provide almost a tenth of a day's iron requirements? Cranberries can help keep the urinary tract free from infection and raspberry is a good remedy for upset tummies.

SERVES 4   ① ④ ⑥ ⑧ ⑨

1 litre (1¾ pints) cranberry juice

50g (2¾oz) agar or vegetarian gelatine

100g (3½oz) fresh raspberries

4 fresh mint leaves

1 Put the cold cranberry juice in a saucepan. Add the agar or vegetarian gelatine and bring to the boil gently. Cook for 3 minutes and leave to cool.

2 Divide the fresh raspberries between four individual serving glasses (keep eight back for decoration) and pour the cooled jelly on top.

3 Leave to set in the refrigerator and, when ready, decorate with two fresh raspberries on each portion, along with the fresh mint leaves.

You can make this jelly with any clear fruit juice.

FAT: 0.5G (4%) • PROTEIN: 0.5G (1%) • CARBOHYDRATE: 41G (14%)
FIBRE: 1G (3%) • VITAMIN C: 218% • IRON: 8% • POTASSIUM: 3%
CHOLESTEROL: 0

Buckwheat Pancakes Stuffed with Ham, Egg and Cheese

Here is a well-balanced and fun dish that the kids will love and can even learn to make themselves. With 100 per cent of their daily fibre requirement, and almost the full quota of protein, it is stuffed with nutrients that help keep the whole body in tip-top health. It contains parsley, which is probably the most neglected everyday herb, but it is so powerful that it can even correct vitamin deficiencies. Parsley, which is an excellent lung tonic, is very soothing for asthma sufferers.

SERVES 4 ② ③ ④ ⑤ ⑥

75g (2¾oz) buckwheat flour

25g (1oz) white flour

1 pinch of salt

1 egg, beaten

250ml (9fl oz) milk

4 tsp olive oil

For the filling:

4 eggs

4 tsp olive oil

4 slices organic ham

80g (3oz) Gruyère cheese, grated

50g (1¾oz) fresh parsley, chopped

1 To make the pancakes, sieve the flours together into a bowl with the pinch of salt, then create a well in the middle. Add the beaten egg and a little of the milk and start to stir the flour into the centre. Add more milk and whisk until you have a smooth batter.

2 Heat a pancake pan, splash in a little of the olive oil and pour in enough of the batter to cover the bottom and make the pancake. Cook on both sides until brown but not crispy. Make four pancakes this way.

3 For the filling, fry the eggs in the olive oil. Layer the filling inside the pancakes, starting with the slice of ham, then the egg and finishing with grated cheese and chopped parsley, reserving some cheese to sprinkle on top.

4 Fold the pancakes in half and sprinkle a little more Gruyère over the top half. Cook under a hot grill, just long enough to melt the cheese. Serve with mangetouts and a grilled tomato.

FAT: 24G (35%) • PROTEIN: 29G (99%) • CARBOHYDRATE: 22G (7%)
FIBRE: 2G (100%) • VITAMIN A: 30% • CALCIUM: 40% • FOLATE: 27%
CHOLESTEROL: 80%

Strawberry Fool

This summer pudding is based around strawberries, which contain lignin – a substance that can lower cholesterol levels and protect against cancer of the colon. It binds with the bile acids to remove them and is highly recommended for diabetics. Always a favourite with kids, strawberries can also protect against viruses, preventing, for example, cold sores, and are said to prevent damage to DNA – the genetic material of cells that makes us all who we are and gives children their individual tastes and characteristics.

SERVES 4 ① ② ④ ⑤ ⑧

250g (9oz) fresh strawberries

juice of 1 lemon

300g (10½oz) fromage frais

3 egg whites

50g (1¾oz) icing sugar

1 Wash and dry the strawberries. In a food processor, blend them with the lemon juice and fromage frais. Whisk the egg whites and just as they begin to stiffen, gradually add the sifted icing sugar.

2 Gently fold this mixture into the blended strawberry mix and pour into four individual serving dishes. Leave to set in the refrigerator for an hour and serve very cold with the Honey and Fig Loaf *(see page 112)*.

FAT: 2G (17%) • PROTEIN: 7G (23%) • CARBOHYDRATE: 29G (10%)
FIBRE: 4G (19%) • VITAMIN C: 56% • CALCIUM: 19% • POTASSIUM: 20%
CHOLESTEROL: 2%

POWER JUICES

The Eco-challenger

SPROUTED ALFALFA, TOMATO, LETTUCE AND MINT

The so-called Father of all Foods, alfalfa is packed with nutrients because its roots can travel as deep as 125 metres (125 yards) into unpolluted earth. It is rich in vitamin B12, making this juice excellent for non-meat eaters, and contains a natural fluoride to prevent tooth decay. The taste can be too sprouty for some people, hence the name of this juice. Disguise it with a splash of Worcester sauce if necessary. It will be worth your while, especially if you are thinning on top, because this juice stimulates hair growth. The tomatoes help flush out toxins and lower cancer rates, and their vitamin E is a valued anti-ageing antioxidant.

MAKES 2 X 200ML DRINKS   ② ④ ⑤ ⑥ ⑧ ⑨

600g (1lb 5oz) organic tomatoes
100g (3½oz) celery stalks
100g (3½oz) lettuce
50g (1¾oz) alfalfa, sprouted
handful of fresh mint leaves

Juice all the above and drink straight away while the live enzymes are still active.

> VITAMIN C: 120% • VITAMIN A: 60% • IRON: 30%
> VITAMIN E: 13% • POTASSIUM: 106% • CHOLESTEROL: 0

Ginger Boost

GINGER, BEETROOT, CARROT AND ECHINACEA

The lovely blood red-orange colour of this energizing juice is a sign of an abundance of vitamins and minerals. Beetroot strengthens the immune system, and is rich in blood-building iron. Vitamin A in carrots is a cancer-fighting antioxidant that will also promote healthy skin and nails and help regulate hormones. Ginger helps to beat off chills and improves nutrient absorption. If feeling low, add echinacea, the antibacterial, antifungal herb, to fight off infection.

MAKES 2 X 200ML DRINKS   ① ③ ④ ⑧

1 tsp chopped fresh ginger
500g (1lb 2oz) carrots
250g (9oz) raw beetroot
20 drops echinacea tincture (optional)

Juice all the above and drink straight away. To maintain optimum health, drink twice a week.

> VITAMIN A: 1,410% • VITAMIN C: 60% • FOLATE: 33%
> POTASSIUM: 137% • IRON: 22% • CHOLESTEROL: 0

Get-up-and-go

APPLE, CINNAMON AND CABBAGE

An excellent tonic for the digestion, this power juice can heal inflamed tissue and will soothe the colon, stomach lining, ulcers and heartburn. Fresh cabbage juice can protect the prostate gland and help relieve the symptoms of skin allergies and eczema. High in bone-strengthening calcium, plus vitamins A and C, this energizing drink also contains vitamin U, which can help to relieve colitis but is rapidly destroyed, so drink immediately once juiced.

MAKES 2 X 200ML DRINKS   ② ③ ④ ⑥ ⑨

600g (1lb 5oz) apples
300g (10½oz) white cabbage
¼ tsp ground cinnamon

Juice all the above and drink straight away while the live enzymes are still active.

> VITAMIN A: 6% • VITAMIN B6: 18% • VITAMIN C: 110%
> CALCIUM: 10% • IRON: 8% • POTASSIUM: 76% • CHOLESTEROL: 0

The Red Devil

CRANBERRY JUICE, RASPBERRY AND PAPAYA

Cranberries reduce the acidity of urine and keep the urinary tract in men and women free from the bacteria that can cause painful and recurrent infections, including cystitis. They can also help prevent kidney stones. Raspberries provide natural pain relief and the pepsin enzyme in the papaya aids digestion by helping to break down proteins and other foods in the stomach. This drink can help guard against stomach ulcers, especially for those taking large daily doses of aspirin, a drug that can irritate the stomach lining.

MAKES 2 X 200ML DRINKS ② ④ ⑧ ⑨

300ml (½ pint) cranberry juice
200g (7oz) raspberries
200g (7oz) papaya

Blend all the above together and drink.
If you have a urinary tract infection, try to drink this every day.

• VITAMIN A: 8% • VITAMIN C: 170% • FOLATE: 10% • IRON: 6% • POTASSIUM: 43% CHOLESTEROL: 0

Tropical Fruit Smoothie

BANANA, MANGO AND ALMOND

High in magnesium and potassium, bananas have strong antibiotic properties, can lower cholesterol and strengthen the stomach lining. Mango is richer in cancer-fighting vitamin A than any other tropical fruit and will also help maintain healthy reproductive organs. The king of nuts, the almond is a rich source of monounsaturated fats, which keep blood cholesterol levels low. Cancer clinics tell their patients to eat at least ten a day.

MAKES 2 X 200ML DRINKS ① ② ④ ⑥ ⑧ ⑨ ⑩

400g (14oz) mangoes
100g (3½oz) bananas
300ml (½ pint) almond milk (or soya milk)
25g (1oz) almonds, roasted and crushed

Blend all the ingredients together and drink straight away while the live enzymes are still active.

VITAMIN A: 160% • VITAMIN B3: 17% • VITAMIN C: 100% • IRON: 10% MAGNESIUM: 31% • POTASSIUM: 83% • CHOLESTEROL: 0

Kiwi Quencher

KIWI, APPLE AND WHITE GRAPE

In traditional Chinese medicine, kiwi fruit is one of the foods used to treat breast cancer. It has more vitamin C and zinc than oranges. Grapes are packed with potent anti-cancer agents and apples can help lower cholesterol, stabilize blood sugars and keep the cardiovascular system healthy. This juice packs a huge vitamin C punch and will help alleviate stress and boost your resistance to disease.

MAKES 2 X 200ML DRINKS ① ④ ⑥ ⑧ ⑨

200g (7oz) kiwi fruit
200g (7oz) sweet dessert apples
200g (7oz) white grapes, seedless

Juice all the above and drink with breakfast.

VITAMIN C: 230% • CALCIUM: 4% • IRON: 4% • POTASSIUM: 66% • ZINC: 2% CHOLESTEROL: 0

Energy**Booster**

Energy levels are always a reflection of the quality of food you eat. To boost your energy levels, cut out refined sugars, coffee and alcohol and identify possible food intolerances that may be depleting your energy stores. Here, the dandelion leaves in the first course encourage body cells to make more energy. The cod is rich in B vitamins – especially B1, which helps convert the carbohydrates you eat to more energy – and the dessert is made from energy-giving, potassium-rich bananas.

DANDELION AND PANCETTA SALAD *(see page 52)*

COD FILLET WITH BUTTER BEAN MASH *(see page 60)*

BANANA AND ROSEMARY TATIN *(see page 108)*

Immune**System**Supporter

The immune system protects the body against infection and cancer. Recurrent and chronic infections are a sign of weakened immunity and the most common cause is nutritional deficiency. Vitamin A protects the surfaces of the skin, respiratory and gastrointestinal tracts, which are the body's first defence against invading micro-organisms. Vitamin C increases the production of interferon, which boosts natural defences. This menu is rich in these nutrients, and also contains liquorice, which further boosts resistance to infection by supporting the adrenal glands.

SHIITAKE SOUP *(see page 36)*

MONKFISH SCALLOPS AND OYSTERS WITH LIQUORICE SAUCE *(see page 62)*

ROASTED CELERIAC WITH SAGE *(see page 104)*

PASSION FRUIT SALAD *(see page 116)*

Stress**Buster**

An important antioxidant that is used in tissue growth and repair, Vitamin C
also plays a crucial role in the production of anti-stress hormones.
In addition, it protects against the harmful effects of pollution, enhances
immunity, boosts the absorption of iron and helps the body fight off infection.
Here, all three courses are packed with this multi-role nutrient.

GRILLED MACKEREL WITH GREEN SAUCE *(see page 42)*

◆

CHICKEN PROVENÇALE *(see page 74)*
PARSNIP AND HORSERADISH MASH *(see page 100)*

◆

SUMMER HONEY AND LAVENDER CRÈME BRULÉE *(see page 113)*

Healthy**Heart**

This low-fat, low-cholesterol menu proves you can have your cake and eat it —
as long as you substitute healthy ingredients in place of the high-fat versions.
The creamy garlic soup will help reduce your risk of heart disease. You should
try to eat fish at least twice a week, and in this fish recipe, the potassium in
the sea bass will help regulate heartbeat. Being overweight increases your risk
of heart disease but the fennel side dish is a natural appetite suppressant.
The dessert is very low in cholesterol.

AIGO-BOULIDO (CREAMY GARLIC) SOUP *(see page 34)*

◆

ROASTED SEA BASS WITH LENTILS, LEEKS AND A
WARM TOMATO VINAIGRETTE *(see page 60)*
BRAISED FENNEL *(see page 107)*

◆

RHUBARB AND PLUM TART *(see page 118)*

Colon**Cleanser**

An estimated 15 per cent of the population suffer from irritable bowel syndrome (IBS). Symptoms range from abdominal pain to alternating constipation and diarrhoea, excess mucus production in the colon and nausea. The causes can include food allergies, stress and lack of fibre. This high-fibre menu is full of nutritious ingredients that also taste delicious. You can even serve this menu to your friends.

CHICKPEA, LIME AND CORIANDER SALAD *(see page 50)*

◆

IMAN BAYILDI (TURKISH STUFFED AUBERGINES) *(see page 92)*
BROWN RICE

◆

PINEAPPLE AND PAPAYA ICE CREAM *(see page 116)*

Bone**Up**

A diet that is high in protein, fats and sugar can inhibit the uptake of calcium, and while good quality cuts of organic meat are an excellent source of this crucial mineral, too much meat, coupled with too many soft drinks and too many refined grain foods, will actually flush it out. The lamb is packed with phosphorous which, together with calcium and fluoride, protects against osteoporosis. Vitamin A is also important in the formation of bones and teeth. Here the yams alone provide 680 per cent of the minimum recommended daily allowance and even the handful of fresh mint in the strawberry soup will further boost calcium absorption.

TARTARE OF SALMON WITH FRESH LIME JUICE *(see page 46)*

◆

COSTOLETIE D'AGNELLO AL PARMIGIANO *(see page 84)*
TIAN OF SUMMER VEGETABLES AND GLAZED YAMS
(see pages 102 and 104)

◆

STRAWBERRY SOUP WITH RED WINE *(see page 111)*

Section**Three**

EATING FOR HEALTH

The only sickness that exists in the body today is toxicity, and healthy cells, nourished properly, are immune to such attacks.

Michio Kushi, *The Cancer Prevention Diet*

The **Immune** System

The secret of true health lies in a strong immune system, which will fight off infection, orchestrate the body's healing processes, and even regulate the rate at which you age. A strong immune system is vital: deaths from infectious diseases in the UK and the US have doubled in the last decade, one in three people suffer from allergies (a sign of weakened immunity), and cancer rates are on the rise.

The outward signs of a weakened immune system are easy to see.

There are plenty of signs that warn of impaired immunity, and you don't have to be a doctor to recognize any of them. Fatigue, lethargy, repeated infections, slow wound-healing, allergies, chronic diarrhoea, thrush and inflammation are all easy-to-spot clues. They prove, too, that weakening the body's own defence mechanisms leaves it vulnerable to virtually every type of illness and disease.

The immune system is both complex and fascinating, and there is a delicate balance between a strong, healthy system and an overpowering one that can itself cause disease. It is possible to become ill if your immune response is too strong or directed at the wrong target. Many disorders, including allergies, lupus, pernicious anaemia, rheumatoid arthritis and even diabetes have all been linked to an inappropriate immune response. This can happen when the immune system fails in its primary task – to recognize the difference between harmless cells and chemicals and foreign or dangerous substances.

The immune system is not just one organ or even a group of organs. It is a highly organized system of various organs, systems and cells, including white blood cells, bone marrow and the lymphatic vessels and their organs, which all interact in a complex way. The immune system also involves specialized cells in different body tissues and specialized substances, called serum factors, that are present in the blood.

There are two types of immunity, known as innate and adaptive. Innate immunity, which is present at birth, is the first line of defence against micro-organisms. The skin, for example, naturally secretes mucus to keep out unwanted germs, while the stomach produces acid for the same job. Adaptive immunity is acquired, either through immunization or after you have successfully fought off an infection: what fascinates immunologists is how your immune system remembers every invader it has faced since you took your first breath.

Think of the immune system as an army made up of different regiments with their own jobs to do. This is how it works.

THE LYMPHATIC SYSTEM

About one-sixth of the body is made up of the space between the cells. This is known as the interstitium, and fluid within it is called the interstitial fluid. It is this fluid that flows through the lymphatic vessels to become the lymph. The lymphatic vessels, which drain waste products from the tissues, run in parallel to the arteries and veins. They take the lymph to the lymph nodes to be filtered. In the lymph nodes, important cells called macrophages engulf and destroy foreign particles, including micro-organisms and cell debris. The lymph nodes also contain white blood cells which, when a foreign invader is detected, fire into action to make the antibodies that will protect the body.

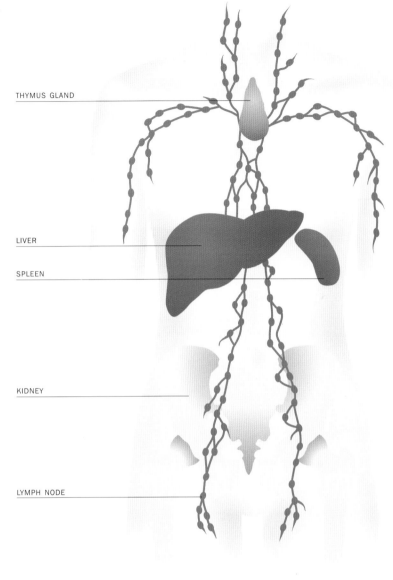

THYMUS GLAND

LIVER

SPLEEN

KIDNEY

LYMPH NODE

Fighting the Common Cold

The common cold is a general inflammation of the mucous membranes of the respiratory passages. Highly contagious, it can be caused by a variety of viruses. Healthy adults should suffer no more than two colds a year because the immune system remembers strains it has fought off and produces antibodies to protect the body. However, new generations of viruses crop up each year and even old ones can easily trick the body's defences, because even the slightest change to a virus's chemical make-up will help it through your body's first line of defence. Poor nutrition, which weakens the immune system, is the most widespread cause of colds. If you have more than two colds a year you definitely need to support your immune system. To prevent a cold, take vitamin C with the bioflavonoid quertin on a regular basis, and at the first sign of infection take zinc. Eat foods that are rich in vitamin B6, to boost the production of the antibodies that fight infection.

The body's frontline defence, the immune system protects against harmful substances and micro-organisms. Bacteria and cell debris are detected in the lymph system and are destroyed by specialized cells produced in the lymph nodes and in the spleen. The whole system is orchestrated by the thymus gland, which also produces specialized cells, called T-cells, to destroy invading bacteria.

The **Immune** System

THE ORGANS

The thymus gland, which lies just above the heart, controls much of the body's immune function. It secretes hormones that regulate the immune system and produces T-lymphocytes (T-cells – see illustration below) which are another form of white blood cell. When immunity is dangerously impaired, the level of T-cells in the body drops. The spleen is the largest mass of lymphatic tissue in the body. The size of a fist, it lies in the upper left abdomen behind the lower ribs and works hard to produce white blood cells and destroy bacteria and cellular debris. It mops up and destroys old blood cells and acts as the body's blood bank.

SPECIALIZED SERUM FACTORS

When specialists talk about immunity, you hear them mention the terms interferon and interleukin II. These are chemicals produced by the various white blood cells. T-cells produce interferon and macrophage cells produce interleukin. These substances help enhance immunity and are called serum factors. They activate the white blood cells to seek out and destroy cancer cells and viruses.

IMMUNE BOOSTERS

Stress takes its toll on the immune system by increasing the production of fight-or-flight hormones, including adrenaline, which, in turn, depress the activity of white blood cells and cause the thymus gland to shrink. The more prolonged the stress, the greater the damage to the immune system.

To counter this vicious circle, make sure you get plenty of good quality sleep (important immune-enhancing compounds are released during sleep) and practise meditation. Your immunity gradually declines with age, but overwork, sleeplessness and prolonged stress will accelerate the rate of decline.

DIET

To support your immune system, each day your diet needs to include 3–5 servings of fruit and vegetables, a heaped teaspoon of seeds (sunflower or pumpkin), a clove of garlic and eight glasses of water. You should drink herbal teas and fruit juices in preference to coffee and tea and eat shiitake mushrooms three times a week, unless you have a fungal infection (*see pages 36 and 44 for shiitake recipes*). Reduce the

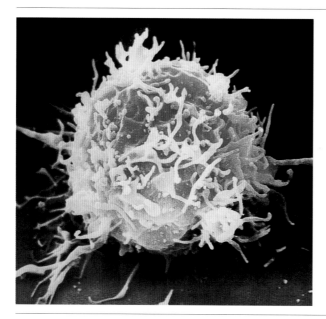

Natural-born Killers

Never mind the film: the Natural Killer Cells (NKC) are the SAS of your army. They destroy cells that have become cancerous or infected by viruses and are the body's first line of defence against cancer. They work with T-cells (left) to fight disease by destroying cancerous cells. The levels and activity of these important cells are low in people who suffer from Chronic Fatigue Syndrome, cancer and any kind of chronic viral infection. To increase the activity of your Natural Killer Cells, stop smoking, eat more green vegetables, eat regular meals and maintain a healthy body weight. Make sure you get more than seven hours of sleep each night, exercise regularly, eat a vegetarian diet and get tested for any nutritional deficiencies, which you can then reverse with supplements.

amount of sugar in your diet (eat less than 50g/1oz a day) and cut out alcohol. Studies of human white blood cells show they are much slower to mobilize to areas of infection in those who have consumed even a modest amount of alcohol. High cholesterol levels can also stop white blood cells from getting to infected sites and slow down the rate at which they multiply. Vitamin A promotes thymus health and can prevent the organ from shrinking. It also maintains the surfaces of the skin, respiratory and gastrointestinal tracts, which, when healthy, act as a barrier to micro-organisms. Natural sources of vitamin A include yellow fruits and vegetables, organic milk and eggs. Vitamin C will enhance immune response by increasing the production of white blood cells and interferon. Citrus fruits, broccoli, kale, peas, tomatoes, orange juice, guava, papaya and kiwi fruit are all excellent food sources of vitamin C.

SUPPLEMENTS

To keep your immune system strong, take a good multivitamin containing at least 10,000 IUs (international units) of vitamin A, 150mg of vitamin E, 25–50mg of B vitamins, 200–400mg of calcium and magnesium, 10mg of zinc and 50mcg of selenium. In addition, take 1–3g a day of immune-boosting vitamin C and an antioxidant supplement so that you are taking a daily total of 20,000 IUs of vitamin A and betacarotene, 150mg of vitamin E, 15mg of zinc and 100mcg of selenium.

HERBS

Lots of herbs have a potent effect on the immune system. The best-selling immune herb is echinacea (*see page 19*), which activates the macrophage white blood cells. It is also an antibacterial and antiviral agent, but should only be used in the short term. In Chinese medicine, astragalus root is used to treat viral infections. It appears to work well where the immune system has been damaged by chemicals or radiation.

Eating plenty of garlic, shiitake mushrooms, citrus fruit and broccoli will keep your immune system in peak condition, providing plenty of antioxidant vitamins A and C as well as other antiviral, protective substances.

The root and leaves of the echinacea plant have long been valued as a support for the immune system.

The **Digestive** System

The saying "You are what you eat" is well known, but many health practitioners qualify it by saying "You are what you *absorb*". The process of digestion is complicated and involves many different organs and chemical processes. Many people eating a traditional Western diet have a dysfunctional digestive system, meaning that they do not absorb all the nutrients they need from their food.

Throughout history, food has always been a major part of any celebration as this picture by Hess shows.

You will not get the full benefit of any of the nutrients you eat – either from your diet or from supplements – if your digestive tract does not work properly. Naturopaths estimate that 70 per cent of all diseases are caused or exacerbated by problems in the gut. While maintaining good colon health is as simple as eating a high-fibre diet, drinking plenty of water and maintaining a healthy balance of microflora in the gut, many of us struggle to digest and eliminate our food properly. In the US, over 4 million people frequently suffer from constipation. In the UK, Irritable Bowel Syndrome (IBS), which causes alternating constipation and diarrhoea, is now believed to be responsible for as much sick leave as back pain.

The main function of your digestive system is to break down the food you eat so that your body can absorb the nutrients it needs and flush out those that are surplus to requirements. This process, which is both chemical and mechanical, starts in the mouth, where the saliva contains special enzymes that begin the process of breaking food down. The simple act of chewing signals to all the other gastrointestinal components to swing into action ready for digestion.

Once your food has been sufficiently chewed, it is transported to the stomach, which churns it up and mixes it with the digestive juices. Food does not leave the stomach until it is in a semi-liquid state, which is called chyme. This then moves into the 7m (21ft) long small intestine, where the minerals are absorbed first, followed by the carbohydrates and proteins. Finally, in the last section of the small intestine, fat, cholesterol and the bile salts that aid digestion are absorbed.

Both highly complex and truly integrated, the digestive system runs from the mouth to the anus, involving, along the way, the salivary glands, the liver, the gall bladder and the pancreas. Since it also controls the elimination of waste and toxins, when the digestive system is sluggish or goes wrong, as well as causing internal problems, it can adversely affect the condition of your skin, hair and nails, and can even cause acne. It can also exacerbate a variety of other ailments, including arthritis and haemorrhoids.

DYSBIOSIS

In a normal gut, there is over a kilo (3 lb) of bacteria, including so-called "friendly" bacteria as well as harmful ones. Some health practitioners believe in certain conditions the balance may be thrown out, leading to a condition called dysbiosis, which can accelerate the onset of conditions such as IBS.

Typically, the beneficial bacteria are outnumbered by those that can cause problems. At best, the good bacteria make up only a third of the population of microflora in the intestines. At worst, especially after the prolonged use of antibiotics or after years of a diet high in refined foods and sugar, levels of friendly bacteria may be so low they are virtually undetectable.

With dysbiosis, there are so few beneficial bacteria populating the gut that numbers of the pathogenic bacteria, such as *Escherichia coli*, which make unhealthy byproducts are allowed to

Good Guys, Bad Guys

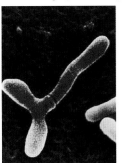 

The good guys are the bifidobacteria (left). When present in sufficient quantities in the gut, they help lower cholesterol levels, prevent food poisoning, alleviate constipation and help the body to digest lactose (the sugar in milk) and to manufacture important B vitamins, including folic acid, which is now believed to protect against heart disease. These bacteria also prevent diarrhoea and produce chemicals that alter the acidity of the gut, making it harder for the "bad guy" bacteria (right) to flourish.

flourish and increase to dangerously high levels.

Conditions believed by some to stem from dysbiosis include acne, Chronic Fatigue Syndrome (*see page 174*), Irritable Bowel Syndrome, food allergies (*see page 168*), depression (*see page 178*), Candida (thrush), rheumatoid arthritis and colitis.

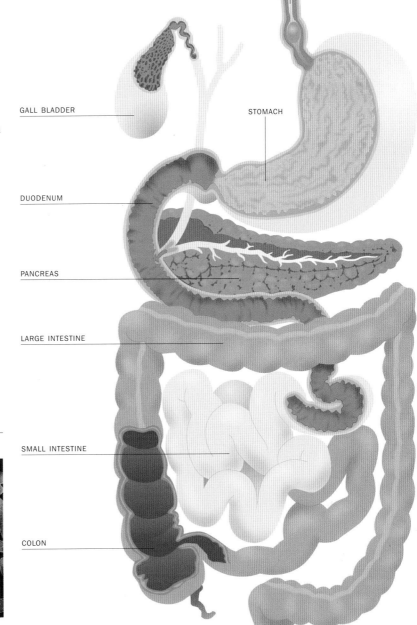

OESOPHAGUS

GALL BLADDER

STOMACH

DUODENUM

PANCREAS

LARGE INTESTINE

SMALL INTESTINE

COLON

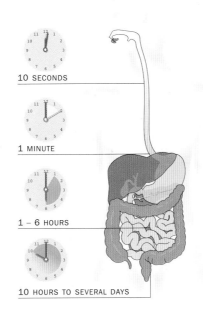

10 SECONDS

1 MINUTE

1 – 6 HOURS

10 HOURS TO SEVERAL DAYS

From the time food enters the mouth to when it leaves the body, the digestive process can take between 10 hours and several days. It includes both mechanical operations, such as chewing, and chemical actions, for example, breaking down fats into their constituent parts.

The **Digestive** System

Foods such as bananas, honey, asparagus, artichokes and tomatoes are all rich natural sources of FOS, which has probiotic properties, meaning that it feeds the friendly bacteria in the gut.

in Japan. Although FOS taste sweet, like sugar, they act in the body like fibre because they have a molecular structure which passes, undigested, from the stomach into the large intestine.

Once there, FOS act as a nourishing food for the beneficial gut bacteria that, when flourishing, help the body to make protein, assist the digestion and absorption of nutrients, and support the immune system in its work to fight infection and prevent harmful bacteria from multiplying.

FOS occur naturally in foods such as bananas, onions, garlic, artichokes, barley, tomatoes, rye, honey and asparagus, but while eating these foods on a regular basis will help you maintain healthy digestion, if you already have digestive problems, you would have to eat them by the bucketful to get a significant therapeutic dose. Fortunately, supplementation is simple. FOS is sold either as a powder or a syrup. For maximum benefit, the brand you buy should be at least 95 per cent pure. If you are not sure what you are buying, check with the manufacturer. Adults can take 1g a day.

DIET AND BOWEL FUNCTION

Ailments that may be caused by prolonged constipation include diverticulosis, haemorrhoids, hernia, boils, bowel cancer, cellulite, indigestion, bloating, obesity, varicose veins, headaches, insomnia, halitosis and flatulence. The continued use of commercial laxatives is not the answer, because far from relieving the problem, they simply perpetuate it, often leading to physical dependence. Chemical laxatives work by stimulating the bowel nerves and this eventually weakens the muscles. A healthier alternative is to add fibre-rich ground psyllium seeds to your food and drink plenty of water. Avoid dairy products which, being mucus-forming, only make the problem worse. In addition, take regular, moderate exercise to encourage the movement of waste through the intestines and prevent the accumulation of toxins, which, if not eliminated, will make you ill.

If you suffer from any of the conditions just mentioned, you need to investigate natural ways to repopulate your intestine with friendly microflora.

Lots of people know that eating natural yogurt can help with this. What they don't know is that for the yogurt to provide any beneficial bacteria it must be live and very few labels will tell you exactly which strain of bacteria you are eating. To tackle ailments caused by a disrupted digestive tract, you need to consult a nutritionist to make sure you get not only optimal amounts of these bacteria but exactly the right strains.

PROBIOTIC FOODS

The widespread problem of dysbiosis has led to much interest in substances called fructooligosaccharides, whose tongue-twister of a name is, thankfully, always shortened to FOS. The first of the new so-called "functional foods" that have been engineered to promote health in a specific way, they are a complex sugar derived from plants and already used in around 500 foods

If you do suffer from constipation, eating extra bran may exacerbate the problem, especially if the lining of your gut has been stripped of friendly

Camomile tea soothes the digestive tract.

bacteria by antibiotics or other conventional drugs, leaving it very sensitive. Lots of people step up the fibre content of their diet by stepping up their intake of bran, but they forget to increase the amount of water they drink in proportion, which can be very harmful.

Aloe vera juice can help repair a damaged gut lining, but read the label or check with the manufacturer to make sure the product you buy is high in the mucopolysaccharides that soothe and heal the lining of the gut. Drink a quarter of a glass in the morning and again at night. Nettle tea, which is a good liver tonic, will also help to gently stimulate the digestive tract. Drink three cups a day if you suffer from erratic bowel movements.

Magnesium, which is crucial for proper bowel function, is frequently lacking from most people's diets – in fact magnesium deficiency is the second most common deficiency in both men and women.

Good natural sources include seafood, wholegrains, soya products, dark-green leafy vegetables and nuts.

The most frequent cause of diarrhoea is the presence of bacteria that are alien to the digestive tract. These usually come from food poisoning, or eating food that has been poorly refrigerated, undercooked or is partially rancid. Diarrhoea can also be caused by prolonged use of laxatives, emotional stress, food allergies, heavy drinking, too much caffeine, infection, pancreatic problems, prescription drugs and parasites. If you have diarrhoea, avoid milk products, which will make it worse. When you have recovered, eat foods that are particularly rich in nutrients, such as wheatgerm and watercress, as well as foods that can help to restore healthy gut flora, such as natural yogurt or sauerkraut.

HERBS

Herbs that help restore normal digestive function include ginger (especially useful if you have stomach cramps), chamomile, agrimony and goldenseal, which is a powerful antibacterial agent.

Detox Plan

The best way of flushing toxins and wastes from the body is a fast, which is usually the first step in any colon-cleansing programme. To detoxify your system, drink the juice of a fresh lemon squeezed into a cup of warm water both first thing in the morning and last thing at night. The herb pau d'arco will help restore the acid/alkaline balance of the colon and promote healing. It tastes very "planty", but has excellent detoxifying properties and is also useful in treating persistent Candida (thrush) infection.

For a healthy bowel, eat plenty of magnesium-rich foods such as fish, prawns and other seafood, brown rice and spinach.

Skin
Disorders

They may not be life-threatening, but skin conditions such as acne, psoriasis and eczema cause much distress to sufferers and can be notoriously difficult to eradicate completely. However, new research is revealing that diet plays an unexpectedly important part in skin problems and sufferers can help themselves by adopting a healthy diet, supplemented where necessary with vital minerals and vitamins.

The skin is not just a protective wrapping – it is the body's largest organ. As well as regulating body temperature and sensing both painful and pleasant stimuli, it shields us from the harmful effects of the sun and prevents many substances, including micro-organisms, from entering the body, and so is our first true line of defence. Many skin disorders can be diagnosed just by looking at them, yet dermatology remains medicine's poor relation and a significant number of skin diagnoses turn out to be wrong.

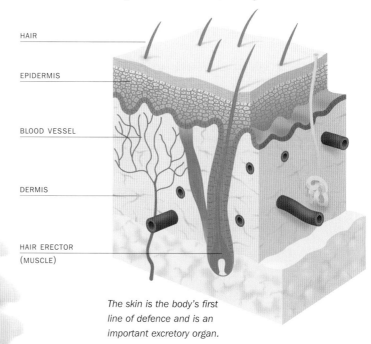

HAIR

EPIDERMIS

BLOOD VESSEL

DERMIS

HAIR ERECTOR
(MUSCLE)

The skin is the body's first line of defence and is an important excretory organ.

ACNE

The most common of all skin disorders, acne is becoming more prevalent in adults. Characterized by the recurring formation of blackheads, whiteheads and pimples (mostly on the face but sometimes on the shoulders, chest and back, too), it is caused not by junk diets or poor hygiene but by hormones and bacterial infection.

Pimples or spots form close to the surface of the skin pore when the cells that line the hair canal produce an excess of keratin – the fibrous protein that is the main component of the outermost layer of skin. This keratin begins to block the canal, forming a blackhead if the blockage is only partial, and a whitehead if the blockage is total. A bacterium called *Propionibacterium acnes* (*P. acnes*) starts to overgrow and releases the enzymes that cause the painful and unsightly inflammation.

Most people think acne is caused by too much of the male hormone, testosterone, but new research suggests that the problem is not one of increased testosterone levels, but, more accurately, is one of how the skin metabolizes this hormone. The skin of acne sufferers has now been found to exhibit greater activity of an enzyme called 5-alpha-reductase that converts testosterone to a more potent form called dihydrotestosterone (DHT).

Intestinal health also plays a role in acne: in one study, 50 per cent of patients with severe acne had increased blood levels of toxins absorbed from the gut. Yet doctors persist in prescribing antibiotics for acne. Why? In many cases, the *P. acnes* bacterium has become resistant to any antibiotic treatment and, as well as being ineffective in such cases, the prolonged use of antibiotics will almost certainly upset the delicate balance of the microflora in your digestive tract.

Foods that help those prone to acne include nuts and shellfish, which are rich sources of zinc. Bananas are beneficial, helping to restore levels of friendly bacteria in the gut, and broccoli is an excellent plant source of calcium, which acne sufferers lack.

HOW TO HELP

A low-salt, calcium-rich diet can help. So will vitamin A, which helps maintain the surface of the skin, and zinc, which is an efficient antibacterial agent. Calcium-rich foods include green leafy vegetables, organic dairy products, broccoli, tofu and shellfish. Natural good sources of vitamin A include yellow fruits and vegetables and fish from unpolluted waters. Rich sources of zinc include wheatgerm, peanuts, shellfish, pecan nuts and turkey. Bananas can help repopulate the good bacteria in the gut, but for severe infections, probiotic FOS supplements are recommended.

ROSACEA

A chronic skin disorder in which the cheeks and nose are abnormally flushed and covered in acne-like eruptions, rosacea is more common in women than men. It affects adults aged between 30 and 50 and, although no cause has been identified as yet, sufferers have been found to lack B vitamins, especially B2 (riboflavin), which not only energizes cells, but works within them to clear out toxins.

Gastrointestinal disorders may also be to blame, with insufficient hydrochloric acid in the stomach – a condition called hypochlorhydria – frequently cited as a contributing factor.

Skin Disorders

Foods such as almonds, meat, fish and yogurt are all good sources of vitamin B2, which research has shown that people with rosacea lack. Drinking fennel tea helps ease rosacea by flushing toxins out of the system.

Hydrochloric acid helps to break down nutrients in the stomach. Too little can impair the absorption of vitamins and minerals and can affect the digestion of protein.

HOW TO HELP

If you suffer from rosacea, avoid hot drinks and spicy foods, which may exacerbate the skin's flush reaction, and apply tea tree oil to the rash. Eliminate refined sugars, fried foods and anything that contains trans-fatty acids, including margarine and synthetically hydrogenated vegetable oils. Supplement your diet with a good B-complex vitamin and eat plenty of foods rich in riboflavin (vitamin B2) such as cheese, chicken, organic milk and yogurt, fish, pork, almonds and organ meat. Brewers' yeast and wheatgerm are also rich in B2. A probiotic, such as acidophilus, and digestive enzymes can both help compensate for the low levels of hydrochloric acid. Herbs that may help include chamomile and fennel – drink these as herbal teas.

ECZEMA

Characterized by chronically itchy and inflamed skin that becomes very red, dry and scaly, eczema, or atopic dermatitis, is believed to affect up to 7 per cent of the population. It is becoming increasingly common among children and, while sufferers spend a fortune on topical creams, most patients will improve on a diet that eliminates the most common food allergens. In children, allergies to milk, eggs and peanuts account for over 80 per cent of eczema cases. These allergies are believed to create "leaky gut", a condition in which the consequence of increased permeability of the intestinal lining is an over-burdened immune system that has to deal with food molecules which would not normally have penetrated through the lining of the stomach.

In adults with eczema, low zinc levels may also play a role. There is usually a family history of the condition and most sufferers go on to develop asthma and/or hay fever. There is also a direct link between eczema and a compromised immune system, so any measure that boosts the body's natural defences will help. Sample white blood cells taken from the skin of patients with eczema, for example, have been shown to have an abnormality that causes them to release higher amounts of histamine and other allergic compounds. An overgrowth of the common yeast, *Candida albicans*, has also been linked with eczema.

HOW TO HELP

The successful treatment of eczema requires a two-pronged approach. You need to reduce the burden on the immune system by cutting out known allergenic substances and you also need to prevent the body's tendency to release histamine and other allergic factors in the skin. Through a process of elimination, identify the foods you are allergic to and avoid them for at least a year. Research has shown that in many cases, not eating the offending food for 12 months effectively robs it of its potency and the sufferer appears to outgrow the allergy. Next, replace animal products with fatty fish, especially salmon, mackerel, herring and halibut. Take zinc and vitamin A and E

People with eczema benefit from a diet based around zinc-rich fish and shellfish. They should avoid milk, milk products and peanuts.

supplements and substitute tea, coffee and sugary soft drinks with green tea, three times a day. Liquorice can also help (*see page 62 for a zinc-rich fish and liquorice recipe*).

PSORIASIS

In 50 per cent of psoriasis cases, there is a family history of the condition. Psoriasis affects men and women equally and generally first appears in the late twenties. As well as affecting the skin, causing a red rash covered with overlapping silvery scales, it can also cause an inflammatory form of arthritis.

The areas most often affected are the scalp, the back of the wrists, the elbows, knees, bottom and ankles. Caused by a basic defect in the skin, the cells replicate too quickly to be shed properly. They replicate 1,000 times faster than normal skin, and it is the resulting accumulation of cells that produces the characteristic silvery scales.

The rate at which cells divide is controlled by a delicate balance between two compounds: cyclic adenosine monophosphate (AMP) and cyclic guanidine monophosphate (GMP). Higher than normal levels of GMP cause cells to divide too fast.

Higher levels of AMP reduce the rate of cell replication. Bizarrely, studies also show a drop in the levels of both AMP and GMP causes the cells to divide too fast again, so a correct balance between these compounds and normal levels of both are crucial for cells to divide at the usual rate.

Other factors that either cause or contribute to psoriasis include poor protein digestion, bowel toxaemia, impaired liver function, too much alcohol, too much saturated animal fat in the diet, nutritional deficiencies and stress.

How to help

Making efforts to stop over-burdening the liver is a good first step. Cut out alcohol, which has definitely been linked with psoriasis, and drink organic nettle tea, which is an excellent liver tonic. Fish oils, which are rich in the omega-3 fatty acids, have been shown to improve psoriasis significantly. Following a gluten-free diet with plenty of fibre can also help, and so can plenty of sunlight. Decreased levels of both vitamin A and zinc have been identified among sufferers and there is growing evidence that vitamin D plays an important role in cell replication. Natural food sources of vitamin D include salmon, mackerel, tuna and egg yolks.

As well as avoiding alcohol, people with psoriasis should increase their vitamin D intake with plenty of oily fish and eggs. Nettle tea helps to cleanse the system.

Cold Sores

Caused by the herpes simplex virus, which invades and reprogrammes healthy cells, cold sores are an unsightly condition. The good news, however, is that the immune system eventually becomes more efficient at suppressing the virus. If you have cold sores, eat foods high in the amino acid lysine, which has been shown to slow the growth of this virus. These include fish, shellfish, fruit, vegetables, beans and brewers' yeast. Avoid flour, sugar, refined soft drinks, coffee, alcohol and processed foods. During an outbreak, do not eat foods that contain the amino acid L-arginine. These include chicken, cereals, almonds and chocolate. Some citrus fruits may also exacerbate the infection.

Allergies and Intolerance

True allergies provoke anaphylactic shock: a life-threatening, but thankfully rare, severe reaction of the immune system to certain drugs, food substances or insect stings. Food intolerances are much less dramatic, but far more common. Many health practitioners believe that they are a growing problem and that they are an underlying factor in disorders ranging from headaches and digestive problems to depression and chronic fatigue syndrome.

Pollen, shown magnified here, can provoke an allergic reaction.

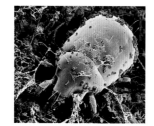

The housedust mite, which feeds on dust and dead skin.

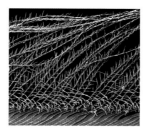

Close-up view of a long-eared owl's feather.

Allergies are triggered when susceptible individuals are exposed to common allergens such as pollen, animal dander (particles of skin and feathers) and the housedust mite.

Dog skin and hair seen through a microscope.

The word "allergy" simply means altered reactivity. It refers to any inappropriate response by the immune system to a substance that is not usually harmful. When your body mistakenly identifies a harmless food, for example, as a toxic invader, the immune system goes into overdrive to produce an abundance of histamine, which increases blood flow in the capillaries supplying the membranes. This then causes swelling and congestion. The body's white blood cells start to overreact too and end up doing more damage than the offending substance.

When this happens, the allergic response itself has become a condition, the symptoms of which can include coughing, wheezing, nasal congestion, itching, headache, fatigue, hay fever, asthma, eczema, high blood pressure, constipation, dizziness, nausea, abnormal tiredness, hives and other skin rashes.

The substances that provoke an allergic response are called allergens. The most common of these are pollen, dust, animal hair, certain metals, food additives and chemicals found in household soaps, detergents and washing powders.

Food, too, can provoke an allergic response. The most common offenders are chocolate, peanuts, dairy products, eggs, shellfish, strawberries and wheat. If you are allergic to these, the reaction is so severe that you will already know about it. However, a major allergy can often mask a more minor one and when you clear the main problem, you may still be plagued by an allergy to foods you had thought you could tolerate.

Allergy or Intolerance?

It is important to make the distinction between a food allergy and a food intolerance. In an allergy, the immune system generates an antibody response to the allergen. Food intolerance on the other hand is the inability to digest and process certain foods correctly and is usually caused by a lack of certain digestive enzymes. Food intolerance can, though, lead to a food allergy if undigested particles of food enter the bloodstream where they can cause an allergic reaction.

If you are highly allergic to certain foods, you will already know all about it. You may have a dramatic allergic response as soon as you start chewing the food and will have already eliminated it from your diet. If your reaction is not as extreme, you may suspect you are allergic to one of the foods you eat more than twice a week. For most people, the most common offenders are likely to be wheat, eggs, citrus fruit, dairy products, tea and coffee. Choose one of these and exclude it from your diet for six days. (If you're testing a number of foods, test them individually and make sure you have a week of rest between testing different substances.) To help you keep track of your reactions and what you are testing, keep a food diary. Also, remember if you are allergic to one member of a particular food group, you are likely to react in the same way to

Some of the most common foods that trigger allergies include strawberries, chocolate, shellfish and eggs.

other members of that group. For example, if you react to potatoes, you may also react in the same way to tomatoes, peppers and aubergines (all part of the *Solanaceae* family).

When you embark on allergy testing through elimination, you can expect to feel worse before you feel better. You may have headaches or even flu-like symptoms. These are a good sign – they show you are definitely sensitive to the food you have just eliminated.

In healthy people, the lining of the intestine generates new cells faster than any other tissue in the body. When they work properly, these cells make a permeable lining that acts as a filter, allowing the nutrients we need to pass through, but blocking those nutrients and toxins that will cause an allergic response if they get into the bloodstream. The lining can do this because it is full of tiny holes. Damage to the intestinal lining can increase the size of these holes and cause a condition known as "leaky gut" in which toxins and foods that should not pass into the blood get through the filter, prompting the immune system to mount an allergic-reaction type of attack.

If left unchecked, a leaky gut can even cause the body's natural defences to mistake your own body tissue for a foreign invader that they then begin to destroy.

If you meticulously write down everything you eat for a week in a food diary, *you will be able to work out what triggers your food intolerances.*

Allergies and Intolerance

Test Yourself

Some doctors believe that at least 60 per cent of Americans suffer symptoms linked to some form of food intolerance. To test yourself for an allergic reaction, relax and then measure your pulse rate. You should count 52–70 beats a minute, which is the sign of a healthy pulse. Now eat the food you want to test. Wait 15–20 minutes and take your pulse rate again. If it has increased by more than 10 beats per minute, eliminate it from your diet for a month and then re-test. When testing any food in this way, always try to eat the food in its purest form. The elimination and re-introduction of a food is the most foolproof way of pinpointing the substances causing an allergic reaction. Allergies run in families, but you can break the cycle if you stop eating the offending food for a minimum of two years. You must be strict about this and when you do re-introduce it, don't eat it more than once every five days or you will have an adverse reaction again.

When the immune system is confused in this way, it will cause an autoimmune disease, a problem that some believe to be at the root of many conditions, including inflammatory bowel disease and arthritis. In trials, children and adults suffering from eczema and asthma that was triggered by food allergy were found to have higher gut permeability. To help repair a "leaky" gut, avoid the foods to which you are sensitive (*see* Test Yourself, *above*).

Tomatoes, aubergines, potatoes and peppers belong to the same plant family. If you are allergic to one, you may be allergic to them all.

HOW TO HELP

The number of adults and children who suffer from food intolerances has increased dramatically in recent years. There are three reasons for this. First, most of us regularly eat too much of a limited number of foods – if you eat the same foods every day, your body gradually becomes intolerant of them. Second, there are high levels of artificial colourings, preservatives, flavourings and stabilizers now added to food, which exacerbate the problem. Third, impaired digestion as a result of a leaky gut is also partially to blame.

To avoid an allergic reaction, first identify and stop eating the foods you know you react to. Food allergies often develop slowly, so in addition rotate the foods you eat, and don't eat the same food more than once every four days. For example, if you eat fish on Friday, wait at least until Tuesday before eating fish again. Rotating foods not only makes you feel better, it will encourage you to be more adventurous in the kitchen and cook with foods that are new to you.

Drinking Nettle and Sorrel soup (*see page 34*) can both help relieve inflammation and clear congestion. It contains vitamin C, which the body needs to help it cope with the overproduction of histamine that results from an allergic response. The soup is also rich in B vitamins, which helps ease allergic symptoms.

Try eating foods rich in quercetin, a bioflavonoid that has been found to stabilize cell membranes, stopping them from seeping histamine into the surrounding blood and tissue. Good natural sources include red onions, shallots, squash, courgettes and broccoli. Quercetin, which is also sold as a supplement, is even more effective when teamed with bromelain, an enzyme found in pineapple that has excellent anti-inflammatory properties and which, incidentally, can help prevent cold sores.

The omega-3 fatty acids found in fish oils and other substances contain potent anti-inflammatory compounds, so if you have an allergic response, eat plenty of salmon, mackerel and flaxseed oil.

Herbs can help prevent an allergic attack. Echinacea supports the immune system, the Chinese herb ginkgo has been shown to be

effective in treating the bronchial constrictions that are typical of an asthma attack prompted by an allergy, and eyebright, as its name suggests, is good for relieving itchy eyes.

You should avoid foods containing additives and colourings, and choose organic wherever possible. In the last 50 years, there has been an explosion in the number of new chemicals in daily use in farming and the environment and many of these find their way into the human body.

Sensitivity to chemicals is believed to be a growing problem: for example,

Ginkgo, the oldest species of tree on the planet, contains anti-inflammatory chemicals that help reduce the severity of an allergic reaction.

many of those who suffer from Chronic Fatigue Syndrome overreact to chemicals. Also, Multiple Chemical Sensitivity (MCS), which is not yet recognized by conventional medicine, has been described by complementary practitioners as the most puzzling disease of the new century. Symptoms range from headaches and depression to flu-like ailments, gastric problems and joint pains. The main culprits appear to be pesticides – particularly organophosphates, which can accumulate in fat. It certainly makes sense to avoid food grown using intensive farming methods as we cannot remain infinitely tolerant of new chemicals that are being pumped into the body.

Finally, there is no simple cure for allergies and they are always worse when you are under stress, so try to control the severity of an attack by learning some form of relaxation technique and practising it every day.

A diet rich in vegetables such as squash, courgettes and broccoli, with plenty of oily fish and pineapple will reduce the sensitivity of the gut and provide vital nutrients for those suffering from food allergies and intolerances.

The **Heart** and **Blood**

The number one killer in both the UK and the US, heart disease accounts for more than 40 per cent of all deaths in the States. We expect so much from our heart, which beats 100,000 times a day to transport oxygen and vital nutrients to every cell in the body, yet we do so little to keep it healthy. Coronary health and diet are closely linked so the good news is that there is much you can do to reduce the chances of heart disease.

SUPERIOR VENA CAVA

AORTA

RIGHT BRONCHUS

LEFT ATRIUM

SEPTUM

MYOCARDIUM (HEART MUSCLE)

The heart is a miracle of engineering that pumps blood first to the lungs to be oxygenated and then out via the aorta round the body to individual cells. Heart disease is now responsible for more deaths in the UK and US than any other illness, and puts a great strain on hospitals and emergency services (above right).

The big breakthrough that nutritionists believe will improve our cardiovascular health and save more lives than any other is the discovery in the blood of a compound called homocysteine. This substance, which is formed during protein metabolism when the amino acid methionine is converted to cysteine, is 40 times a more accurate predictor of heart disease and stroke than cholesterol. Raised levels of homocysteine have been found in the blood of up to 40 per cent of patients suffering from heart disease, for example.

Astonishingly, the discovery is not new: the Harvard scientist who first discovered the importance of homocysteine first published his results 30 years ago.

Homocysteine is believed to damage the arteries by interfering with the blood vessels and causing the build-up of dangerous plaque deposits in the coronary arteries – a condition known as atherosclerosis in which the arteries thicken and harden. Angina, an excruciating pain in the chest,

is often the first outward sign of a heart problem and is almost always due to atherosclerosis, indicating that blood flow has become restricted because the blood vessels have narrowed. High blood pressure is also a symptom of atherosclerosis: it occurs because the heart has to pump harder to get blood through narrowed arteries.

Fortunately, you can use diet and supplementation to help lower homocysteine levels and prevent atherosclerosis. You should follow a diet based on wholegrains and antioxidant fruit and vegetables and reduce your intake of saturated fat (found principally in animal products). Vegetarians tend to have lower blood pressure and lower rates of heart disease and stroke than meat-eaters. Although meat is an abundant source of iron, which is needed to make healthy red blood cells, there are plenty of good vegetable sources of this nutrient.

Raised levels of homocysteine are found in people who are deficient in folic acid, vitamin B6 and vitamin B12. Research shows that taking daily supplements of these nutrients can reduce levels.

The antioxidant nutrients – selenium and vitamins A, C and E – are also important in protecting against heart disease. Vitamin E is believed to be the most important of these, in fact several studies have shown that vitamin E levels in the blood are, again, a more accurate indicator of risk of heart disease than cholesterol levels.

Foods for a Healthy Heart

To lower homocysteine levels eat foods that are rich in folic acid and vitamins B6 and B12. Good sources include:

Folic acid – spinach, asparagus, Brussels sprouts, butter beans, soya beans, organic organ meats, brewers' yeast, root vegetables, wholegrains, wheatgerm, kidney beans, bulgar wheat, oysters, salmon, orange juice, avocados and organic milk.

Vitamin B6 – avocados, bananas, carrots, lentils, brown rice, bran, soya beans, sunflower seeds, tuna, salmon, wheatgerm and wholemeal flour.

Vitamin B12 – organic beef, cheese, eggs, fish, clams, organic milk and dairy products.

For general protection against the risk of stroke and heart disease eat less fatty and processed food and more of foods rich in the following:

Antioxidants – yams, butternut and winter squash, pumpkin, carrots, spinach, broccoli, iceberg lettuce, endive, kale, tomatoes, melon, apricots, mango and papaya.

Selenium – tuna, herring, oysters, clams, sesame seeds, Brazil nuts, sunflower seeds, wholegrains and brewers' yeast.

Magnesium – seafood, wholegrains, dark green vegetables, molasses and nuts.

Potassium – lean meats, red snapper, salmon, yogurt, wholegrains, potatoes, avocados, bananas, apricots, melon, tomato juice, orange juice, peaches, prunes, soya beans, butter beans, Swiss chard, yams, spinach, dried fruits and sunflower seeds.

Iron – eggs, fish, poultry, cherry juice, green leafy vegetables, dried fruits, liver, meat and organ meats.

Magnesium and potassium are both essential for cardiovascular health. Magnesium is readily available in lots of foods, but many people are deficient because they eat a diet high in meat and dairy products as well as processed and refined foods, which have had the magnesium stripped out.

A low potassium and high sodium (salt) diet is linked to high blood pressure. Dietary potassium will lower blood pressure and has been found to be particularly useful in treating people over the age of 65, who often do not respond well to the drugs commonly used to lower blood pressure.

A diet rich in fish, seafood, pulses and fruit and vegetables will keep your heart in top condition.

Energy
Boosters

Can you recall that post-holiday feeling when you were brimming with health and boundless energy? To recreate it all the year round, you need to eat a good diet and take plenty of regular exercise. Research reveals that nutritional deficiencies and food intolerances can deplete energy levels more than was once realized, and that they also contribute to the debilitating condition, Chronic Fatigue Syndrome, which has become so prevalent in the West.

If you identify more with the tired person on the right rather than with the healthy person on the left, your diet may be lacking vital nutrients.

It is important to eat a healthy diet because a deficiency in any nutrient can cause fatigue and make the body more susceptible to infection.

If you have been suffering from a debilitating exhaustion for six months or more and if no other underlying cause has been found, you could have what is now known as Chronic Fatigue Syndrome (CFS).

This condition was only officially named and defined by the United States Center for Diseases Control (CDC) in 1988. In fact, it is anything but new. Still a controversial medical diagnosis, it has been known about since the 1860s, and has flourished under a number of different names. In the UK, for example, it is still called Myalgic Encephalomyelitis (ME). In the credit-mad, spend, spend, spend 1980s it was known as Yuppie Flu. Some people call it Postviral Fatigue Syndrome and others Post-Infectious Neuromyasthenia.

Whatever the name, the symptoms, which come and go, are likely to include a mild fever, a recurrent sore throat, swollen lymph nodes, weak muscles, a recurrent headache, depression, insomnia or an excessive need for sleep, joint pain and prolonged fatigue after any form of exercise.

The reason CFS remains controversial is because scientists still cannot agree on a single cause – there are several theories – and many doctors still believe it to be entirely psychosomatic.

The very latest thinking is that it could be caused by an innate abnormality in regulating blood pressure followed by a viral infection that leaves lasting damage to the immune system. The blood pressure theory came into being following the results of an American study that found that at the point when the heart needs to speed up to deal with exertion, in CFS sufferers it actually slows down. This abnormality cannot be detected by normal tests for blood pressure, but in one study it was present in 22 out of 23 CFS patients. The researchers speculated that a subsequent viral infection then triggered CFS.

The viruses incriminated but still not proven guilty include Epstein-Barr, the human *Herpes simplex* and the Coxsackie B organisms. Orthodox medicine has concentrated its efforts on searching for a viral cause for the condition, while complementary medicine practitioners take steps to reduce susceptibility and to support the immune system of patients so they can deal more effectively with an invading organism.

Both fibromyalgia (FM) and Multiple Chemical Sensitivity (MCS) produce symptoms that are similar to those of Chronic Fatigue Syndrome and the exact diagnosis of your condition will depend on the bias of the doctor you see. In addition, many pre-existing conditions and their treatments can also cause chronic fatigue. Depression has also been found to be the most common cause and CFS has long been recognized as a key feature in food allergies, which have been diagnosed in up to 85 per cent of CFS sufferers.

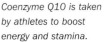

Coenzyme Q10 is taken by athletes to boost energy and stamina.

HOW TO BOOST ENERGY LEVELS

Low blood-sugar levels can cause depression, low energy levels and chronic fatigue. Sufferers should cut down on sugar and refined carbohydrates, cut out coffee and step up their intake of energy-giving protein.

One of the most exciting discoveries in the treatment of chronic fatigue is a powerful antioxidant called Coenzyme Q10 (CoQ10), a vitamin-like substance said to act in the body in a similar way to vitamin E.

Oily fish, nuts and spinach should make a regular appearance in everyone's diet, because they contain Coenzyme Q10 to boost energy.

Energy **Boosters**

If you lack energy, eat plenty of fish, green leafy vegetables, fruit and lean meat, which are all good sources of magnesium.

BENEFICIAL MAGNESIUM

Magnesium is crucial to the activity of both the enzymes and coenzymes involved in the production of energy. Even the slightest deficiency in this important mineral can give rise to chronic fatigue and CFS-type symptoms. A blood sample will give an accurate picture of the body's magnesium levels. Most CFS patients, tested this way, have lower magnesium levels than non-sufferers.

Magnesium is known as the anti-stress mineral. It boosts the uptake of both calcium and potassium, a deficiency of which interferes with the transmission of nerve and muscle impulses, causing irritability and nervousness.

Most foods contain some magnesium, but particularly rich sources include fish, meat, seafood, dairy products, green leafy vegetables, wholegrains, nuts, lemons, figs, apples, apricots, bananas and brown rice. Avoid heavy drinking, which lowers magnesium levels. If you are going to take a supplement, buy a product in which the magnesium is bound to either aspartate or citrate, both of which help fight fatigue.

A coenzyme works alongside an enzyme. An enzyme is a protein that acts as a catalyst to bring about chemical changes. Coenzyme Q10 is needed by every single cell in the body to produce energy and is often taken by athletes to increase stamina and endurance. It boosts circulation, increasing the amount of oxygen received by the tissues. It also increases energy levels, has powerful anti-ageing properties and is believed to help strengthen muscles.

Coenzyme Q10 also bolsters the immune system and has been shown to counter histamine (a substance that is produced in an allergic reaction), which helps it to prevent the allergies that can often cause CFS. Coenzyme Q10 has also been used to treat mental disorders, including depression, another cause of CFS.

Coenzyme Q10 may be taken as a supplement, but good food sources include spinach, tuna, sardines, peanuts, mackerel, sesame, pulses and bran. It is easily destroyed by cooking, storing and processing but marinated sardines (*see page 46*) are an excellent source because no cooking is involved.

Dandelions are rich in vitamin C for energy. Use the leaves in salads and make the petals into wine.

Take up a form of exercise that you enjoy, such as dancing, to boost your energy levels.

fight off disease. Liquorice root, which has strong antiviral properties, will also support the immune system, but only take with a herbalist's advice as in strong doses it may raise blood pressure.

ENERGY-BOOSTING EXERCISE

If you don't suffer from CFS but you do feel tired all the time, you need to take up some form of moderate exercise, which boosts energy levels by releasing endorphins which, in turn, help banish depression. You don't have to start training for the New York or London marathon: 30 minutes of modest exercise, three times a week with a rest day in between will do more than anything else to increase both your stamina and vitality.

'Mushroom' tea

The Kombucha or Manchurian "mushroom" is not a mushroom at all, but a large, flat, pancake-shaped fungus-like growth that is a combination of health-promoting lichen and beneficial bacteria. It has long been used in Asia as a natural energy booster and is fast gaining credence among CFS sufferers worldwide. A potent detoxifier and immune enhancer, it has been said to slow and even reverse the ageing process, help fight diseases including CFS, cancer, Multiple Sclerosis (MS) and AIDS. It is not eaten, but turned into a strong antiviral and antibacterial tea by leaving it to ferment for 7–10 days in a mixture of water, sugar, green or black tea and cider vinegar. Russian researchers have found the tea's antibiotic activity is at its peak after 7– 8 days and kept this way, your mix will produce "daughter" mushrooms, which can then be used to make more tea. There are now 10 million Kombucha tea drinkers worldwide.

VITAMIN C FOR ENERGY

Most animals can make their own vitamin C, but people, apes and guinea pigs must glean theirs from their diet. This valuable substance is a powerful immune enhancer and is essential for tissue growth and repair. It also boosts the absorption of iron, which is critical for both energy production and a healthy immune system.

High doses of vitamin C have been given to CFS patients with good results. For chronic fatigue, a daily dose of 3000mg (1g x 3 a day) is recommended. Good food sources include broccoli, asparagus, dandelion greens (*see Dandelion and Pancetta Salad page 52*), citrus fruits, sweet peppers, green peas, spinach, strawberries, Swiss chard, watercress, pineapple, kale, lemons, kiwi fruit, cabbage, cauliflower and mangoes. Avoid smoking, which seriously depletes vitamin C stores.

HEALING HERBS

Herbal remedies for CFS include Siberian ginseng which, as well as supporting adrenal function, helps increase resistance to stress by boosting the number of T-cells and Natural Killer Cells which

Emotional
Health

Job insecurity, money worries, relationship problems, increasing fragmentation of family life – there are many reasons why we all get depressed from time to time. However, in some people depression is persistent and has no obvious external cause. Many ordinary foods have extraordinary powers and, if you are prone to dark moods, you should consider changing your diet to include foods that promote well-being.

Depression is the most common emotional disorder and it affects a large proportion of the population: 30 million Americans take antidepressants every year. It can be the result of an underlying disorder such as food allergies, or Chronic Fatigue Syndrome (*see page 174*), and it can also be a side-effect of prescription drugs, including the contraceptive pill, anti-inflammatories, tranquillizers and sedatives. Stress is a common cause of depression: researchers now believe we are biologically programmed to react to extreme stress by becoming depressed.

The symptoms typically include disturbed sleep patterns and insomnia, which then set up a cycle of fatigue and depression; digestive disorders, tiredness, headaches and forgetfulness; muscle pain, weight loss or weight gain; and a withdrawal from both work and home life. People who are suffering from depression will no longer take pleasure in the things they used to enjoy. Instead, they feel that they have no control over their lives.

For severe cases of depression, antidepressants can make the difference between life and death (in clinical depression, recurrent thoughts of suicide are common), but they are not recommended for those suffering less severe forms since the side-effects include a dry mouth, abnormal heart rate, bloating, confusion, impotence and loss of libido.

FOODS FOR WELL-BEING

Tryptophan is an amino acid that is needed for the production of vitamin B3 (niacin) and for the manufacture of serotonin, the body's own "feel-good" substance. Tryptophan supplements are still banned in the US after a link between a blood

St. John's wort – the sunshine herb.

disorder and supplements containing the amino acid was found. (Subsequent research suggested the problem was due to other contaminants in these products.) The best dietary sources of tryptophan include brown rice, cottage cheese, meat, peanuts, baked potatoes with their skin, roasted pumpkin, dried sunflower seeds, seaweed, milk, turnip greens and soya.

To convert tryptophan in the body to niacin you need sufficient levels of vitamin B6 (pyridoxine). Foods that are excellent sources of vitamin B6 include avocados, bananas, carrots, lentils, brown rice, bran, soya beans, sunflower seeds, tuna, salmon and wholemeal flour.

All the B vitamins can help fight depression because they help relieve stress, but the most important – folic acid – is the one in which most people are deficient. Natural sources include spinach, asparagus, root vegetables, soya beans, organ meats, wholegrains, bulgar wheat, kidney beans, oysters, orange juice and avocados.

To combat depression, take 800mcg a day, with a vitamin B12 supplement because these work together. Folic acid deficiency can mask a deficiency of vitamin B12 which is common (especially in the over-60s), and can cause confusion, memory loss and apathy. As well as vitamin B foods, fatty acids in fish can help lift mood as they are believed to play a crucial role in brain chemistry, so eat more salmon, halibut, sea bass and sardines.

MINERALS, VITAMINS AND HERBS

Magnesium, found in most foods, but especially in figs, lemons, almonds, nuts, seeds, apples and dark-green vegetables, also helps ease depression by relieving stress. Vitamin C, with its anti-allergy and anti-stress properties, can help for the same reasons, and for people with moderate depression, selenium, which is found in seafood, has been shown to elevate mood.

Described as nature's Prozac, St John's wort is an excellent antidepressant that is very successful in treating mild to moderate depression without causing side-effects. For anxiety, insomnia and restlessness, the herbal remedy Kava kava (*see page 183*) has a very soothing effect helping to promote a feeling of calm and well-being.

5-HTP

A chemical that brings us one step closer to the manufacture of the mood chemical, serotonin, is 5-Hydroxytryptophan (5-HTP), which is available in supplement form and is said to be safer than tryptophan supplements because it is extracted from the seed of an African plant (*Griffonia simplicifolia*). It has been shown to be as effective as and even better than the standard anti-depressant drugs and has none of the unpleasant side-effects. 5-HTP also improves the quality of sleep and increases the release of endorphins which help fight depression.

Combat depression with a diet rich in natural sources of tryptophan, an uplifting protein that helps to improve your mood.

Defeating
Cancer

The word cancer comes from the Greek karkinos, meaning crab, referring to the disease's uneven, sideways progress through the body. The biggest killer after coronary artery disease, cancer is understandably feared. However, research studies have shown conclusively that changing your diet and lifestyle can dramatically reduce your risk of contracting the disease.

To reduce your risk of cancer, avoid industrial pollutants and cigarette smoke, which are both carcinogenic, and only consume alcohol and fatty foods in moderation.

Cancer experts estimate that soon after the beginning of the 21st century, between 40 and 50 per cent of the population will develop some form of cancer during their lives. Yet despite increasingly sophisticated medical intervention, we are still no closer to curing this dreaded disease.

According to the US National Cancer Institute, 50 per cent of all cancers may be preventable through diet and lifestyle changes. This is because colon and rectal cancers, for example, which have reached virtually epidemic levels in the West, are almost unheard of in the East. Only a small percentage of cases of both cancers are caused by a genetic flaw, meaning that the real culprit must be the high-fat, low-fibre diet that is typical in the West. Happily, this means that making changes to your lifestyle and diet can dramatically reduce your risk of cancer. It is in the prevention of cancer that the idea of food as medicine really comes into its own. In his book

The Cancer Prevention Diet, Michio Kushi, an expert on macrobiotic eating and a pioneer of the natural foods movement, states, "The proper place to perform cancer surgery is not in the operating room, after the disease has run its course, but in the kitchen and in other areas of daily life before it has developed.

"By removing certain foods from the pantry and the refrigerator, replacing them with the proper quality and variety of foods, and applying proper cooking methods together with correcting environmental conditions and our daily way of life, we can ensure that cancers and other degenerative diseases do not arise."

Of course this idea is not new: it was Hippocrates, the father of modern medicine, who said, "Let food be thy medicine". He was also the first person to identify cancer some 2,500 years ago in ancient Greece and coined the word *karkinos*, from which our word cancer comes.

BENEFICIAL FOODS

A healthy diet and lifestyle is the cornerstone of your fight against cancer. You should eat less saturated fat and processed foods and increase your intake of wholegrains and fruit and vegetables.

There are many books devoted solely to cancer and diet and here I just want to highlight the three most potent weapons in your armoury – antioxidants, phytochemicals and calcium.

Antioxidants are important because they both mop up and prevent the formation of free radicals, which are unstable oxygen atoms that, if left unchecked, bind with other atoms and produce a form of energy that can damage healthy cells, causing them to mutate. This process sets off the chain of events that can lead to cancer. Environmental factors that promote the formation of damaging free radicals include tobacco smoke, air pollutants, pesticides and solvents.

The most potent antioxidants are the vitamins A, C and E. The trace minerals selenium and zinc have also shown excellent anti-cancer properties. To consume enough antioxidants to protect yourself from cancer, you need to eat at least 3–5 servings of fresh fruit and vegetables every day. As very few people achieve this target, you may want to consider antioxidant supplements.

Phytochemicals, substances that occur naturally in plant foods (*see page 26*), are now believed to reduce cancer risk. They are thought responsible for keeping the number of deaths from cancer in the East much lower than in the West. You are 20 times more likely to die from breast or prostate cancer than people living in Asian cultures who eat a diet rich in phytochemical foods such as soya.

Oestrogen is believed to encourage damaged cells, which can lie dormant for years, to start dividing, developing eventually into cancer. Phytochemicals are thought to supplant harmful oestrogen causing it to be flushed out of the body. Not only can phytochemicals help prevent cancer,

Citrus fruit, vegetables and soya beans contain phytochemicals, beneficial compounds that protect the body from cancer.

some researchers believe they can reverse the changes that cause cancer in the first place, turning mutated cells back into healthy ones.

The most powerful phytoestrogen-rich food is soya. Eat at least one soya product a day, but avoid products that have been genetically modified.

Lots of people supplement their calcium intake to build and maintain healthy teeth and bones, but few realize the mineral may also protect against cancers of the colon and rectum, which are now the third biggest cancer killers in the UK and the second in the US. In one US study of 25,000 people, those who took 1200mg of calcium daily had a 50 per cent reduced risk of colon cancer.

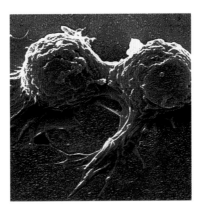

What is Cancer?

Every minute, some 10 million cells in your body are in the process of dividing. Healthy cells know just when to do this and when to stop, but cancer cells lose this ability. Somewhere between one in a million and one in 100 million cell divisions, something goes wrong and a cancer cell is the result. The cells proliferate rapidly and produce a ball of cancer cells that disrupt the healthy tissues around them. The mass of abnormal cells continues to grow to become a tumour which, if untreated, will interfere with the functioning of nearby organs and, eventually, cause death. Two common types of cancer are breast cancer (above left) and lung cancer (above right).

Avoiding **Stress**

Too much stress is to blame for many disorders ranging from insomnia and depression to high blood pressure. If you suffer frequently from stress-related ailments, you need to take a long look at your lifestyle. In particular you should make time for yourself. It may seem indulgent to spend time unwinding with the newspapers but "me time" is an important investment in your own health. So, too, is eating plenty of foods rich in stress-busting B vitamins and minerals such as magnesium and calcium.

Motorway drivers have to be in a constant state of alert watching out for dangers, and stress levels soar as a result.

Events most likely to trigger a stress reaction are job pressures, family arguments, financial worries and deadlines. It is now believed that stress is a factor in 80 per cent of illnesses and accounts for more than two-thirds of visits to the family doctor. The symptoms may include high blood pressure, back and neck pain, dizziness, diarrhoea, insomnia, fatigue, tearfulness, poor concentration, sexual dysfunction, loss of appetite or over-eating.

A modest amount of stress from time to time may sharpen your performance at work or help you pass an exam, but constant stress will eventually kill you. In animal studies, prolonged stress has been shown to kill perfectly healthy heart cells, damage the immune system, raise blood-sugar levels and even cause the bones to thin, increasing the risk of osteoporosis. It is also known that stress increases the number of harmful free radicals in the body.

GENERAL ADAPTATION SYNDROME

Stress upsets the body's equilibrium causing a number of biological changes known collectively as the General Adaptation Syndrome (GAS).

There are three distinct phases to GAS. During the initial, alarm stage, you spend your time worrying that you cannot do everything you know you must do. This phase is short-lived and is caused by the flight-or-fight response our ancestors relied on for survival. You then enter the more prolonged and damaging resistance phase, in which you don't want to do everything you know you must do, and have to push yourself harder to achieve less. During this phase, your blood pressure increases to help you cope with all the demands on you. You may feel you have more energy, but in reality you are running on empty and there is a long-term price to pay – exhaustion – the final stage. When you reach this stage you are well on the road towards a major illness.

All three GAS stages affect the adrenal glands, which regulate hormone levels and can become worn out and exhausted when we place too many unrelenting pressures on ourselves. Recurrent infections and illness, which are the result of an impaired immune system, can also be a sign of stress.

Beat stress the natural way with a diet rich in seafood, oily fish, nuts and fruit and vegetables.

MANAGING STRESS

Changing your diet is probably one of the most effective ways to manage stress. The B vitamins are known as nature's own antidote to stress. They work best together, so as well as eating foods that supply the various B-type vitamins, take a good B-complex combination supplement.

The body uses up vitamin C more quickly than usual during stressful periods. If pressure is prolonged, the tissues could become depleted of this crucial vitamin. You can avoid deficiency by drinking the juice of vitamin C-rich fruits and vegetables, especially kiwi fruit, which are even richer in vitamin C than the oranges that sailors were once given to stop them getting scurvy.

Both calcium and magnesium also play a crucial role in beating stress by helping to lower blood pressure, which rises when you are under pressure. If you're avoiding dairy products, natural sources of calcium include broccoli, tofu, soya beans, okra, shellfish, mackerel, salmon and sardines. Good natural sources of magnesium include seafood, wholegrains, dark-green leafy vegetables and nuts.

LIFESTYLE AND HERBAL REMEDIES

The stress hormones prepare the body for action (called the "fight or flight" response) and the very best way to minimize their negative effects is to burn them off with regular exercise. Try walking or swimming three times a week.

Exercise also releases endorphins, which can help to improve mood. If you are feeling stressed, avoid all stimulants, especially coffee, alcohol and cigarettes. You may think that these substances will help to calm you down, but in fact they do the opposite.

Kava kava, the Pacific Island herb first discovered by Captain Cook, helps to promote a feeling of calm and well-being, especially in times of severe stress and anxiety. A natural tranquillizer, Kava kava can help break the vicious cycle of stress-induced insomnia that is caused by anxiety about poor performance, which in turn generates more stress.

Wild yams are a natural source of DHEA.

DHEA

As we age, it takes our bodies longer to recover from stress. We also have lower levels of a hormone called dehydroepiandro-styerone (DHEA) which researchers now believe can help counter the effects of stress. DHEA is produced by the adrenal glands, which sit on top of the kidneys. It is the most abundant hormone found in the bloodstream and is also thought to have an anti-ageing effect, slowing down the production of fats, hormones and acids. At 40, you have half the amount of DHEA you had at 20, which is unfortunate because animal studies have shown this hormone can counter the damaging physical effects of prolonged stress by restoring levels of the stress hormones back to normal. Most DHEA supplements you buy have been extracted from wild yams,

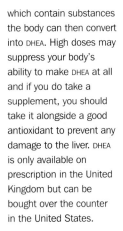

which contain substances the body can then convert into DHEA. High doses may suppress your body's ability to make DHEA at all and if you do take a supplement, you should take it alongside a good antioxidant to prevent any damage to the liver. DHEA is only available on prescription in the United Kingdom but can be bought over the counter in the United States.

Brisk walking in the fresh air dissipates the effect of stress hormones and stimulates the release of endorphins – the body's "feel-good" hormones.

Hormones and Health

The evidence of large-scale hormonal disruption is compelling: worldwide studies suggest sperm counts have dropped by half in the last 50 years. One in seven couples experience infertility, and breast cancer has almost tripled in the last 30 years. Environmental pollutants and use of synthetic hormones for contraception, fertility and menopause management are playing havoc with our hormonal systems. To safeguard your health, avoid pollutants and eat protective foods.

HYPOTHALAMUS   PITUITARY GLAND

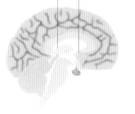

THYROID

LIVER

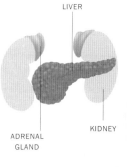

ADRENAL GLAND   KIDNEY

UTERUS

OVARY

TESTES

Scientists investigating conditions linked to disturbed hormones blame the increased and widespread use of chemicals in the environment, food production and pharmaceutical treatments. They believe these chemicals disrupt the delicate balance of the body's hormones.

Hormones serve as the body's messengers. Secreted directly into the bloodstream by different organs, each has a specific job. Collectively, the hormone-producing organs are known as the endocrine system. Its major organs are the hypothalamus, the pituitary gland, the thyroid gland, the parathyroid glands, the islets of the pancreas, the adrenal glands, the testes and the ovaries. In pregnancy, the placenta also acts as an endocrine gland.

The hypothalamus secretes hormones that stimulate the pituitary gland. Some trigger the release of pituitary hormones, for example, while others suppress them.

The pituitary gland is seen as the master gland because it co-ordinates much of the endocrine system, but not all the other

The endocrine system (left) secretes hormones, chemical substances that orchestrate every bodily function including the production of sperm (right).

hormone-producing glands are under its control. Some respond instead to concentrations of certain substances in the blood. The insulin-secreting pancreas, for example, responds to glucose and fatty acids; the parathyroid cells respond to calcium and phosphate.

Most hormones are proteins. Some are steroids, which are fatty substances derived from cholesterol. Both types of hormone work by binding to specific receptors either on the surface of or inside the cell. Once in place, they can change the cell's functioning. They control your growth and development, reproduction and sexual characteristics. They influence the way the body uses and stores energy. They control the volume of fluid and the levels of salt and sugar in the blood. In short, they control everything.

THREATS TO HORMONE BALANCE

Many chemicals, including lots of pesticides, mimic the role of oestrogen in our bodies and stimulate the growth of hormone-sensitive tissue. The effect is to disrupt hormones and confuse the messages they are sending out.

As well has eating fruit and vegetables with pesticide-traces, we also take in oestrogen from meat and dairy products. Animals are frequently

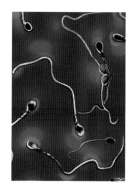

fed a high-protein diet and pumped full of hormones to force rapid growth for more profit. Both meat and dairy products can also act as a storehouse for non-biodegradable toxins that we know disrupt hormone levels.

The use of herbicides and chemicals to produce bigger and better crops carries a hidden price – it is upsetting our hormonal balance.

Lifestyle factors also upset the hormonal balance. Prolonged stress, for instance, produces too much adrenaline and cortisol. Any stimulant, including coffee and cigarettes, results in the body producing cortisol, which increases the production of oestrogen and competes with progesterone for receptor sites, further upsetting the fragile balance of these two important hormones. The long-term consequences of a permanent state of stress can be impaired liver function and an inability to flush toxins from the system.

PROTECT YOUR HEALTH

Your first, most important step is to avoid the chemicals that you know can disrupt hormones. To avoid pesticides and herbicides, for example, always try to buy organic produce. Alternatively, even grow some of your own fruit and vegetables, without the use of chemicals. If you cannot obtain organic foods, always wash and peel fruit and vegetables before you eat them.

Cut back on both meat and dairy foods, which we know can contain hormones, and when you do eat meat, try to buy it from an organic supplier. The non-biodegradable toxins that disrupt hormones accumulate in animal fat, so cutting back on meat and dairy foods will help reduce your risk of a hormone-related condition.

Chemicals used in packaging can seep into the food itself. Reduce this risk by never heating food in plastic containers and by minimizing the contact between plastic and the food you plan to eat. For example, pack and take your vegetables home in paper bags.

The digestive tract produces lots of hormones that work with the nervous system to maintain healthy digestion and absorption. Nutritionists now believe that many of the symptoms usually attributed to hormonal imbalances – including weight gain, water retention, bloating, anxiety and depression – are more likely to be caused by an

undetected digestive problem (*see page 160*). Even those who do have a true hormonal problem will improve more rapidly when the digestion is in optimum health.

It makes sense to investigate natural alternatives to HRT for managing the symptoms of the menopause and to use other forms of contraception instead of the pill. Women approaching the menopause might try eating plenty of soya, citrus fruits, vegetables, cereals, onion, garlic, broccoli, cabbage and cauliflower. These foods contain substances known as phytoestrogens (*see page 26*), which have a natural oestrogenic effect in the body.

Combat PMS the natural way with foods brimming in vitamin B6 such as soya and avocados.

Premenstrual Syndrome

Some 75 per cent of women suffer from premenstrual syndrome (PMS). With the tendency for puberty to start earlier and earlier – the average age is 11 today compared with 17 in Victorian times – PMS will affect women for longer. The symptoms vary between women, but the more common ones include anxiety, irritability, mood swings, fluid retention, breast tenderness, weight gain, acne, fatigue and a craving for sweet foods. Most sufferers have high levels of oestrogen and low levels of progesterone. To reduce excess oestrogen, cut back on meat and dairy products and eat foods that are rich in vitamin B6. These include avocados, bananas, carrots, lentils, brown rice, bran, soya beans, sunflower seeds, tuna, salmon and wholemeal flour. In tests, a daily B6 supplement of up to 800mcg has been shown to reduce oestrogen and boost progesterone levels.

Healthy
Kids

Restaurant "kids' menus" frequently typify the view of what many people regard as suitable food for children: chips, chicken nuggets, burgers, ketchup and sweets – with not a green vegetable in sight. This is a terrible state of affairs since eating well in childhood is crucial for laying the foundations of good health. A healthy diet that is child-friendly need not be a contradiction in terms, and by taking the trouble to prepare wholesome meals you will be setting your child up for a long and healthy life.

A healthy, nutritious diet based on wholegrains, fresh fruit, vegetables, pulses and moderate amounts of lean, organically-produced meat and fish will give your children all the energy and strength they need. It will also increase their resistance to illness. Unfortunately, this is not the kind of diet that most children receive.

In the US, childhood obesity has increased by 54 per cent since 1976. A number of trends have contributed to this. Children take less exercise – many no longer walk to school, for example. Also, eating habits have changed during the last few decades. Many families no longer eat a home-cooked meal together preferring to graze on microwaved, high-fat ready meals. Youngsters who spend all their leisure time glued to the television or the computer and who eat high-fat, low-fibre diets are at risk of developing the same high cholesterol levels as their couch-potato parents. Worse, researchers suspect the unthinkable: that because of their high-fat diet, many children may already be in the early stages of heart disease with arteries that are already narrowed.

BRAND LOYALTY

Children develop brand loyalty from an early age. When they are glued to children's television, they are also being bombarded by junk food commercials. These frequently use cartoon characters to make the product more appealing since, for a young child, there is no distinction between a favourite programme and a clever ad.

To give your child boundless energy, feed her a nutritious diet that contains plenty of fresh fruit and vegetables.

In the US, children spend $2 billion a year on food products and influence the spending of another $75 billion. You can see why manufacturers will spend whatever it takes to catch children as young as they can.

PESTICIDES

Proportionally for their size, children eat more fruit and vegetables than adults do – a child of pre-school age eats the equivalent of around six times more fresh fruit than his or her parents – which should, of course, mean they are healthier. If it wasn't for the widespread use of pesticides and herbicides, they probably would be. However, the use of chemicals by food growers has increased ten-fold in the last half century and children are most at risk from the effects.

The US Environmental Protection Agency (EPA), has identified 66 different carcinogenic pesticides that turn up in the average child's diet. And that's just the ones they can find. Current testing techniques can only identify 40 per cent of possible chemical contaminants and it cannot detect any of the metabolites, which can form when the component chemicals break down in the body and which pose an even greater threat to your family's health than the chemicals themselves.

HOW TO HELP YOUR KIDS

Children copy and learn from their parents. They will eat what you eat, which means that you can lay the foundations of good health in their lives by making healthy choices for the whole family.

If you think that sounds difficult, you are absolutely right, because your children will want to eat exactly the same diet as their friends.

To encourage brand loyalty, manufacturers deliberately produce snacks and sweets in appealing shapes.

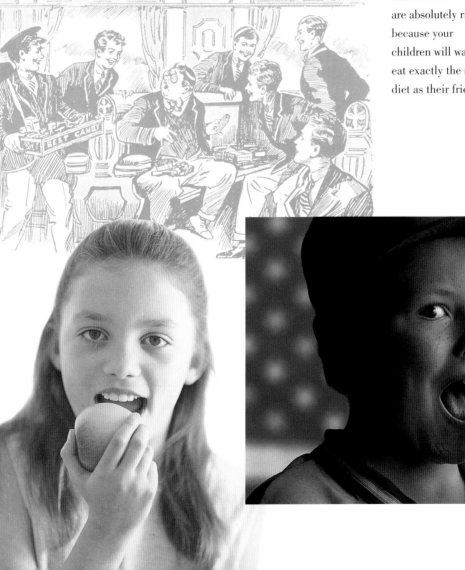

Healthy **Kids**

Use honey as a healthier alternative to sugar for sweetening children's yogurt and other foods.

Many children go through a "faddy" stage and parents worry that they are not getting sufficient nutrients. However, as long as they eat foods from all the different food groups, there should be no cause for concern.

Children need three meals a day, plus wholesome snacks and plenty of pure water. Always serve one vegetable and one grain dish with each meal; for menu suggestions see pages 132–143. Both breakfast and lunch should be larger meals than supper. Preschool children do not have the same capacity as older ones and may prefer to eat little and often, so keep plenty of nutritious snacks to hand, such as yogurt, raisins, cheese cubes and breadsticks.

Your hardest job is to reduce the amount of sugar your child eats. Try to save chocolate, sweets and refined products such as biscuits, cakes and crisps for occasional treats and when cooking for kids, use sugar substitutes such as honey or rice syrup. Offer fresh fruit or yogurt as

Fast food need not be unhealthy. Make pizza for your children with low-fat cheese piled high with delicious vegetables, then finish with a glass of milk.

Scrub all fruit and vegetables thoroughly to remove the skin that may contain traces of harmful herbicides.

dessert instead of sugar-laden puddings. On the other hand, don't let teenagers, especially girls, get hung up about their weight since eating disorders that start in childhood can wreck adult lives. In fact, dump the bathroom scales and explain that eating a healthy diet will help keep them slim. It is better to monitor weight gain by keeping an eye on how clothes fit rather than obsessively counting calories.

More than anything else, eating should be a pleasure. Make mealtimes fun for your child by introducing new exciting dishes and serving food in a fun way. For example, decorating a pizza with a couple of olives and a slice of pepper to make a face (*see pages 132–3*) will tempt even the most reluctant eater.

FOOD SAFETY

Only one per cent of the produce in your supermarket has been tested for pesticides, so if you cannot buy organic produce that has been grown with no chemicals, make sure you wash everything thoroughly. Use a mixture of warm water and vinegar to speed up the breakdown of many pesticides. Always remove the outer leaves of vegetables such as lettuce and cabbage, because these often have a higher concentration of chemicals than the inner leaves. Scrub and peel all root vegetables, including carrots, turnips and potatoes. Scrub and peel any fruits that have been waxed to make them shiny.

Install a water purification system so your family can drink plenty of pure water and make your own fruit juices to avoid the risk of contaminants seeping into the juice from the plastic lining of the carton.

VITAMINS AND MINERALS

Some vitamins, including vitamin C and all the B vitamins are water-soluble, meaning if they are not absorbed by the body that day they are excreted. Your child needs these vitamins every day and you should take this into account when

Avoiding Obesity

Childhood obesity is not only a major problem in the West, but is also a growing problem in countries that have abandoned their traditional, healthy diet in favour of the high-fat, low-fibre and highly processed diet that is to blame for the increase in so many degenerative diseases. To keep your child's weight at an optimum and healthy level, always check the fat content of any food they eat. It is suggested that no more than 30 per cent of a child's total daily calories should come from fat. Each gram of fat is the equivalent of 9 calories. So if, for example, 2 tablespoons of peanut butter contains 15g of fat and 200 calories, you can work out that 15 x 9 = 135. This means that 135 of the 200 calories come from fat. Do this calculation for every meal (read all the labels) and if the calories from fat add up to more than 30 per cent of the total calorie intake, make a determined effort to cut back on the amount of fat your child is eating.

If getting your child to eat fruit is a struggle, serve a fruit smoothie instead. Liquidize half a banana with 3 strawberries and a little apple juice and serve in a tall glass with a novelty straw.

planning meals. Fat-soluble vitamins, which include vitamins A, D, E and K, remain stable at low cooking temperatures, but they are depleted by antibiotics and other prescription drugs.

If you feed children a balanced organic diet, you should not need to give them mineral and vitamin supplements, except when they are ill or run down. When choosing a brand, avoid those that are targeted at children, which may be sweetened with sugar or artificial sweeteners to make them more appealing. Instead find a formulation that is sweetened with honey or rice syrup. Always give your child supplements with food and if they do have to take antibiotics, help repopulate the good bacteria that keep the gut healthy by feeding them live natural yogurt – try the recipe for Home-made Bulgarian-style Yogurt on page 132.

Index
A–Z

Useful **addresses**

Ainsworths Homeopathic Pharmacy
36 New Cavendish Street
London W1
Tel: 0171–935 5330
Mail order homeopathic remedies

The Nutrition Clinic
17 Nottingham Street
London W1
Tel: 0171–935 5700
Award-winning nutritionists specializing in a wide range of disorders

The Centre for Nutritional Medicine
114 Harley Street
London W1N 1AG
Tel: 0171–224 5053
Co-founded by two medical doctors, the centre favours an integrated approach and has a special interest in cardiovascular problems and sports nutrition

McKeith Health Clinic
36 Maryon Mews
London NW3 2PU
Tel: 0171–794 8580
Trained in the US and the UK, the nurtitionist Dr Gillian McKeith is a colon and fertility specialist

Action Against Allergy
PO Box 278
Twickenham
Middlesex
TW1 4QB
Advice on allergy

The Sher Skincare System
30 New Bond Street
London W1Y 9HD
Tel: 0171–499 4022
e-mail: skincare@shet.co.uk
For skincare

The Institute of Optimum Nutrition
121 Deodar Road
London SW15
Tel: 0181–877 9993
Keeps a UK referral register for qualified nutritionists

Revital Health Shops
35 High Road
London NW10
Tel: 0800–252875 (UK calls only.)
Revital health shops in London can obtain anything you're looking for. Catalogue and mail order

The Nutri Centre
7 Park Crescent
London W1
Tel: 0171–436 5122
Europe's biggest resource for complementary health products. There were over 22,000 remedies in stock at the last count and the centre, which supplies by mail order all over the world, has access to over 70,000 book titles

The Green People Company
1 Brighton Road
Handcross
East Sussex
Tel: 01444–401444
Non-toxic organic personal care and household products; catalogue

National Institute of Medical Herbalists
56 Longbrook Street,
Exeter
Devon
Tel: 01392–426022
The Institute will help you to find a medical herbalist in your area

Organics Direct
7 Willow Street
London EC2
Tel: 0171–729 2828
Runs a nationwide organic food delivery scheme in the UK.

The Soil Association
40 Victoria Street
Bristol BS1
Tel: 0117–929 0661
The Soil Association will give you details of organic suppliers in the UK, including local box schemes in your area where you pay an agreed price each week and accept whatever is in season and supplied by the scheme organiser

Author's **acknowledgements**

Lots of people have been generous with their time and encouragement since I first took over writing What's the alternative? for *The Sunday Times*. They include my sister Melissa Clark, Jeremy Langmead, Vera Taggart and Michelle Pamment of *The Sunday Times*, Tony Pinkus of Ainsworths pharmacy; the skin psychologist Helen Sher; Dr Charles Innes, Max Tomlinson, Cally Law, Abby Selby, Anthony and Bharti Haynes, John Deacon, Fildelma Silsbury, Teresa Chris and Lorraine Turner. Thank you too to the Nutri Centre and Revital for assisting with a reference library second to none and to Sophie Collins for thinking of me.